Dictation Practice Workbook Part 1

Second Edition

B W Canning

Pitman

PITMAN BOOKS LIMITED
128 Long Acre, London WC2E 9AN

Associated Companies
Pitman Publishing Pty Ltd, Melbourne
Pitman Publishing New Zealand Ltd, Wellington

First edition 1975
Second edition 1982
Reprinted 1983

Isaac Pitman

Text set in 10/12 pt Linotron 202 Bembo
Printed and bound in Great Britain at The Pitman Press, Bath

ISBN 0 273 01804 3

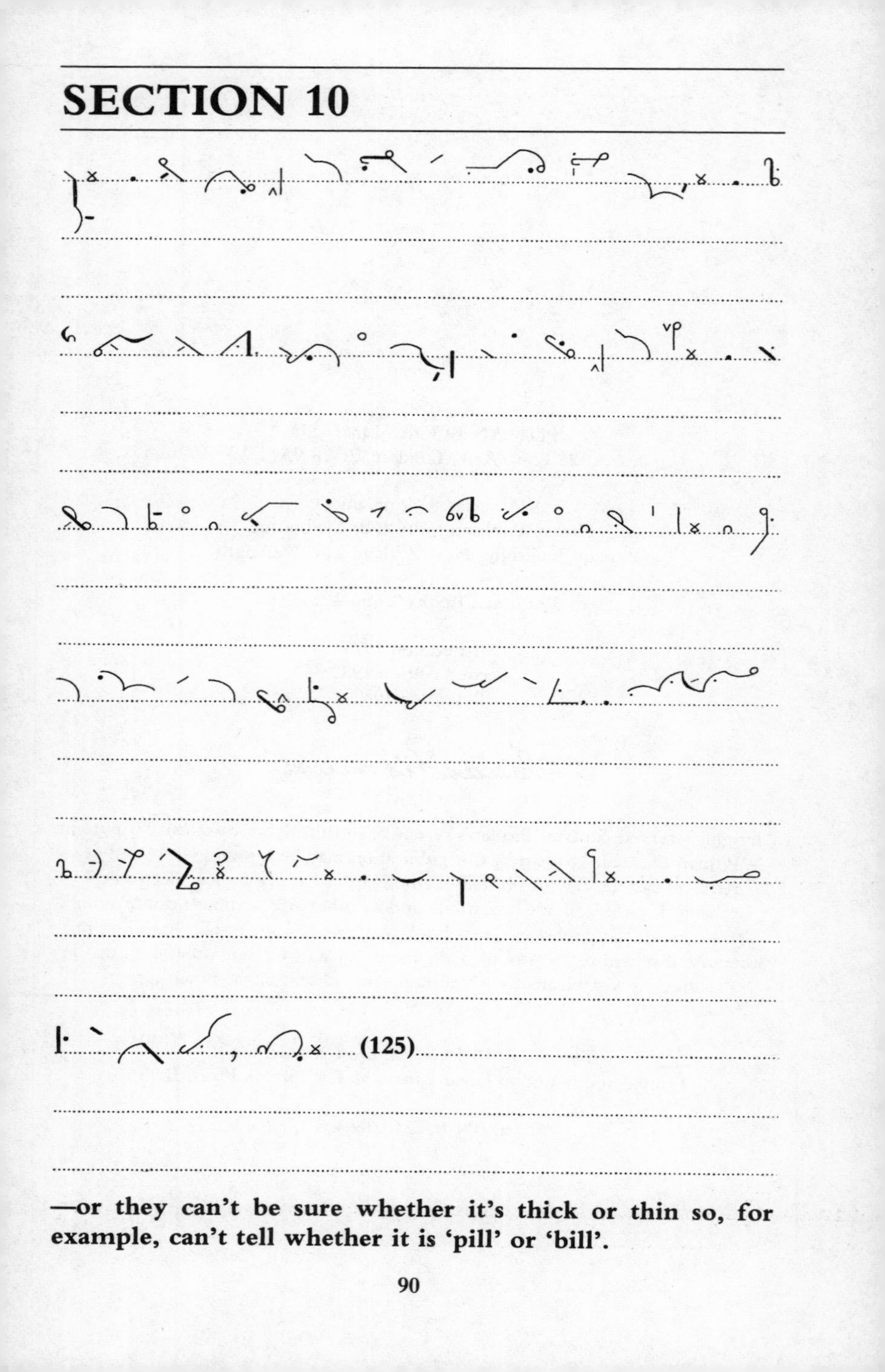

SECTION 10

(125)

—or they can't be sure whether it's thick or thin so, for example, can't tell whether it is 'pill' or 'bill'.

INTRODUCTION

This practical *Workbook* with the pre-recorded material will help students to acquire a quicker, easier and more effective command of Pitman 2000 Shorthand. The workbook should be used in conjunction with *Pitman 2000 Dictation Practice* and while working through *Pitman 2000 First Course*. It will be found an advantage if *Dictation Practice* and the *Workbook* are brought into use one or two days behind the corresponding unit in *First Course* (Second Edition).

The *Workbook* is divided into twenty-one sections which are set out in detail in the Contents pages of *Parts 1* and *2*. Each section comprises:

(1) Short Form Practice

Practice in writing and reading short forms is given in two ways—the short forms are presented in sets of twenty and also in context in sentences. They appear in shorthand in the *Workbook* for checking purposes only. The short forms also appear in conventional printed form in *Dictation Practice*, and they are dictated at 60 w.p.m. and repeated at 80 w.p.m. in the recorded material. It is essential, therefore, that they should be thoroughly learnt before they are written from dictation and finally read back from the shorthand notebook. A cyclic plan is employed in the *Workbook*, which ensures that the short forms already learned are repeated as new ones are introduced, but no short form is left for more than a section or two without repetition. The aim is that by the end of the course, each short form will have received equal practice emphasis.

(2) Phrases

The principles underlying phrasing, and the phrases themselves, are best learned by being read from the workbook, and then by being written in a

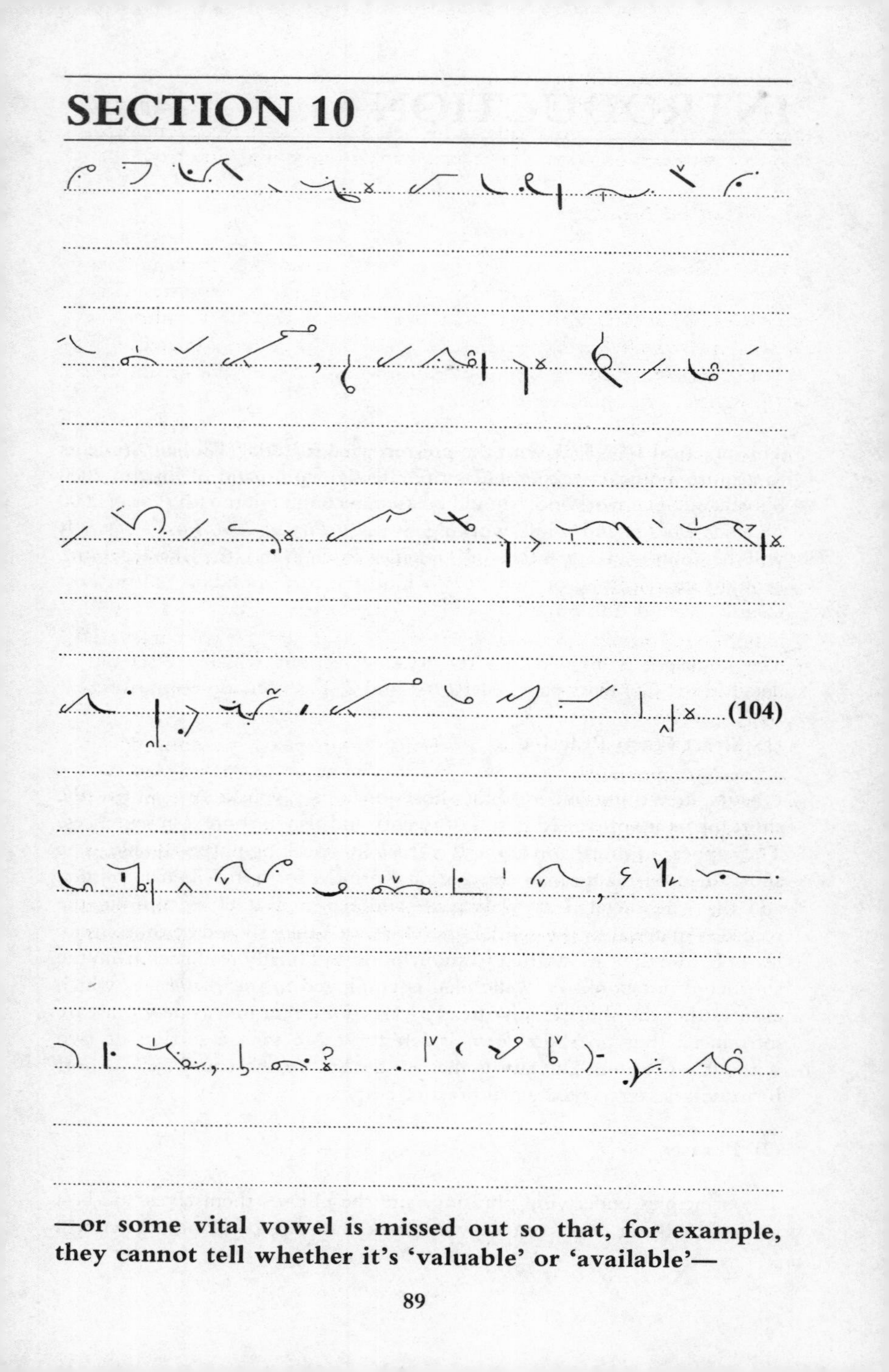

SECTION 10

(104)

—or some vital vowel is missed out so that, for example, they cannot tell whether it's 'valuable' or 'available'—

shorthand notebook from dictation. The workbook should then be used for checking. In the *Workbook* (and in *Dictation Practice*), all the phrases given in *First Course* are included in the shorthand/dictation material, together with additional phrases appropriate to the Unit being covered.

(3) Dictation Passages

The dictation passages for each section are divided into three parts (*a*) easy, (*b*) and (*c*) standard. These passages are included on the cassettes. Each piece has been dictated twice. In Sections 1 to 8 inclusive, the dictation is at 50 w.p.m., repeated at 60; Sections 9 to 14 inclusive are dictated at 60 w.p.m., repeated at 70 w.p.m.; and Sections 15 to 21 inclusive are dictated at 70 w.p.m., repeated at 80 w.p.m.

The easy and standard dictation given in *Pitman 2000 Dictation Practice* appears in shorthand in the *Workbook, Parts 1* and *2*, followed by blank lines for copying from dictation.

How to use Pitman 2000 Dictation Practice with Workbook Parts 1 and 2 (Second Edition)

The following method of working is suggested to improve accuracy and increase speed:

i Read the shorthand from the *Workbook* using *Dictation Practice* when necessary.
ii Copy the shorthand of the *Workbook* from slow dictation, into a shorthand notebook.
iii Use the first copy line in the *Workbook* for writing the shorthand from dictation at the first speed.
iv Use the second copy line in the *Workbook* for writing the shorthand from dictation at the second speed.
v Go back to the first speed, and this time write the passage in a shorthand notebook without reference to the *Workbook*, then read back and check.

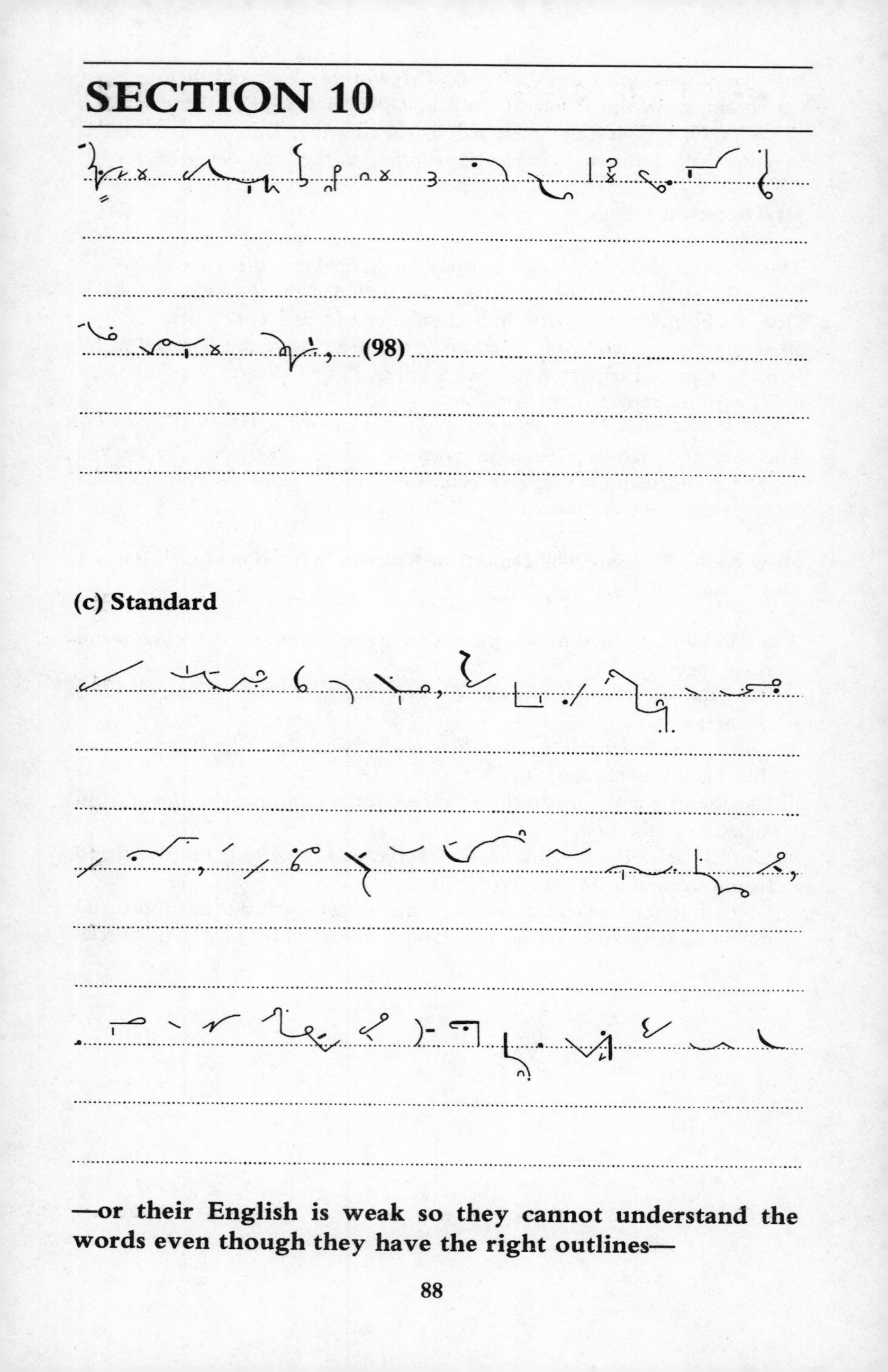

SECTION 10

(98)

(c) Standard

—or their English is weak so they cannot understand the words even though they have the right outlines—

CONTENTS

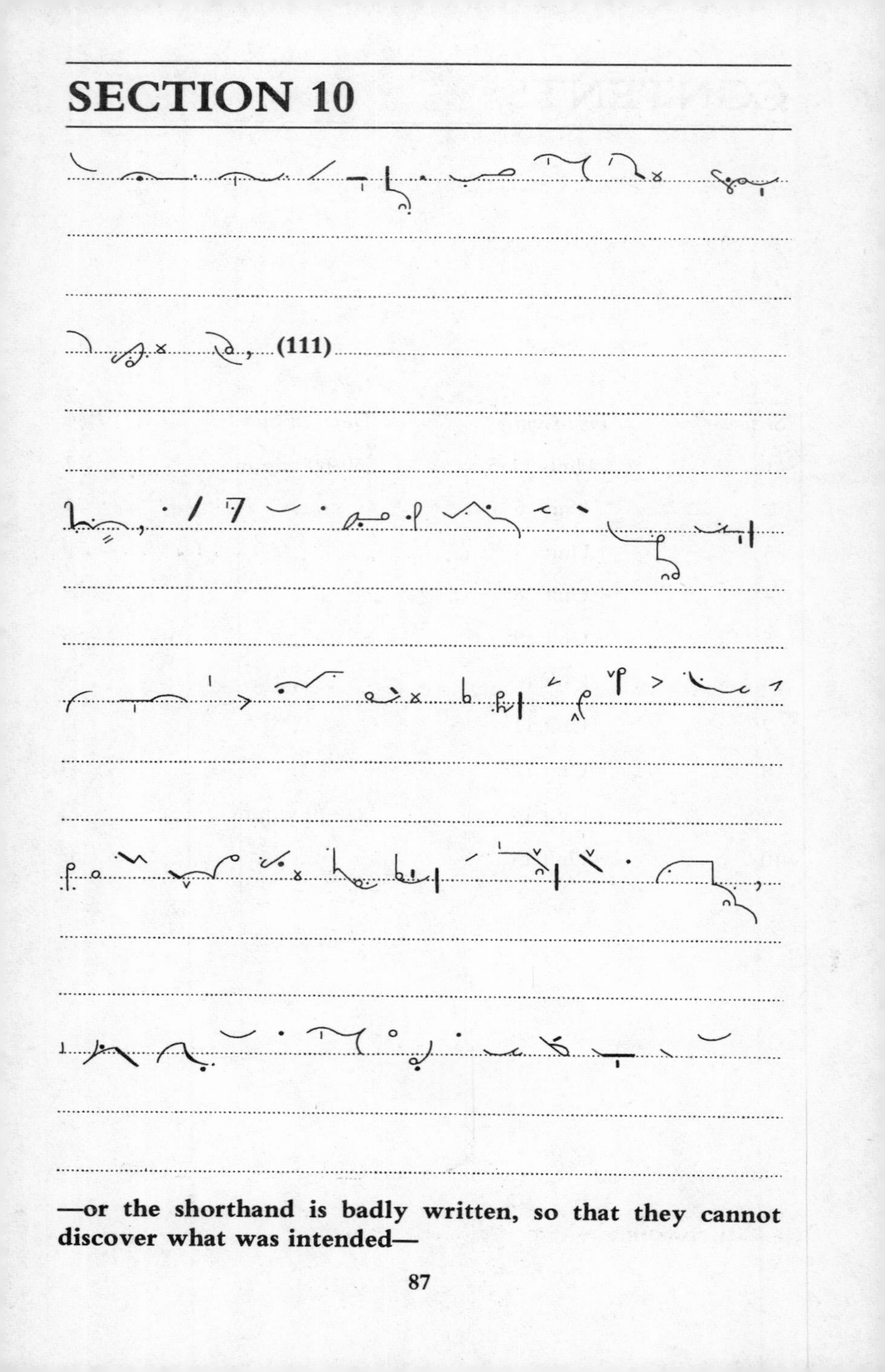

SECTION 10

(111)

—or the shorthand is badly written, so that they cannot discover what was intended—

SECTION 1

Units 1 to 5 of *Pitman 2000 First Course*

1 SHORT FORM PRACTICE

(a)

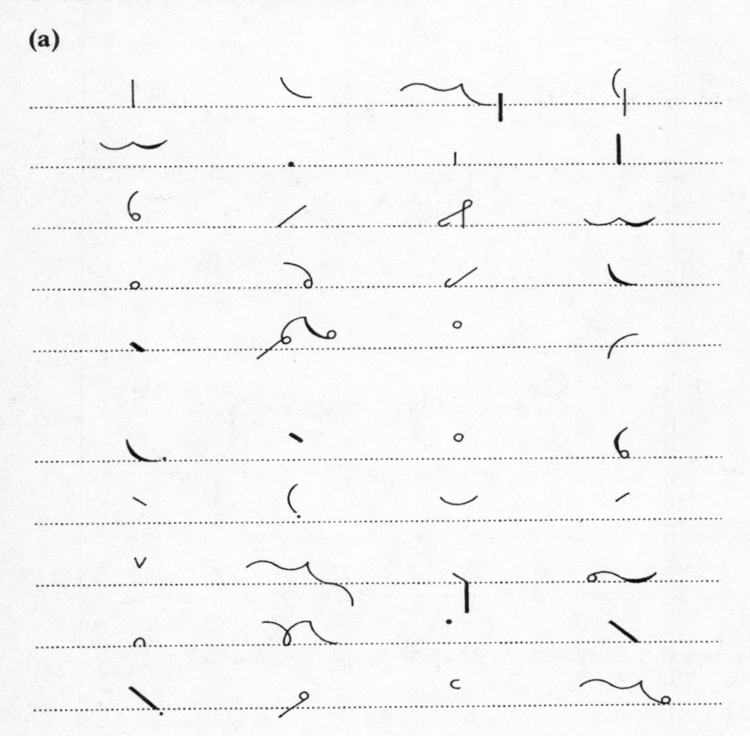

(b)

i .... **(11)** ....

ii .... **(10)** ....

iii .... **(15)** ......

Read the outlines while you write them.

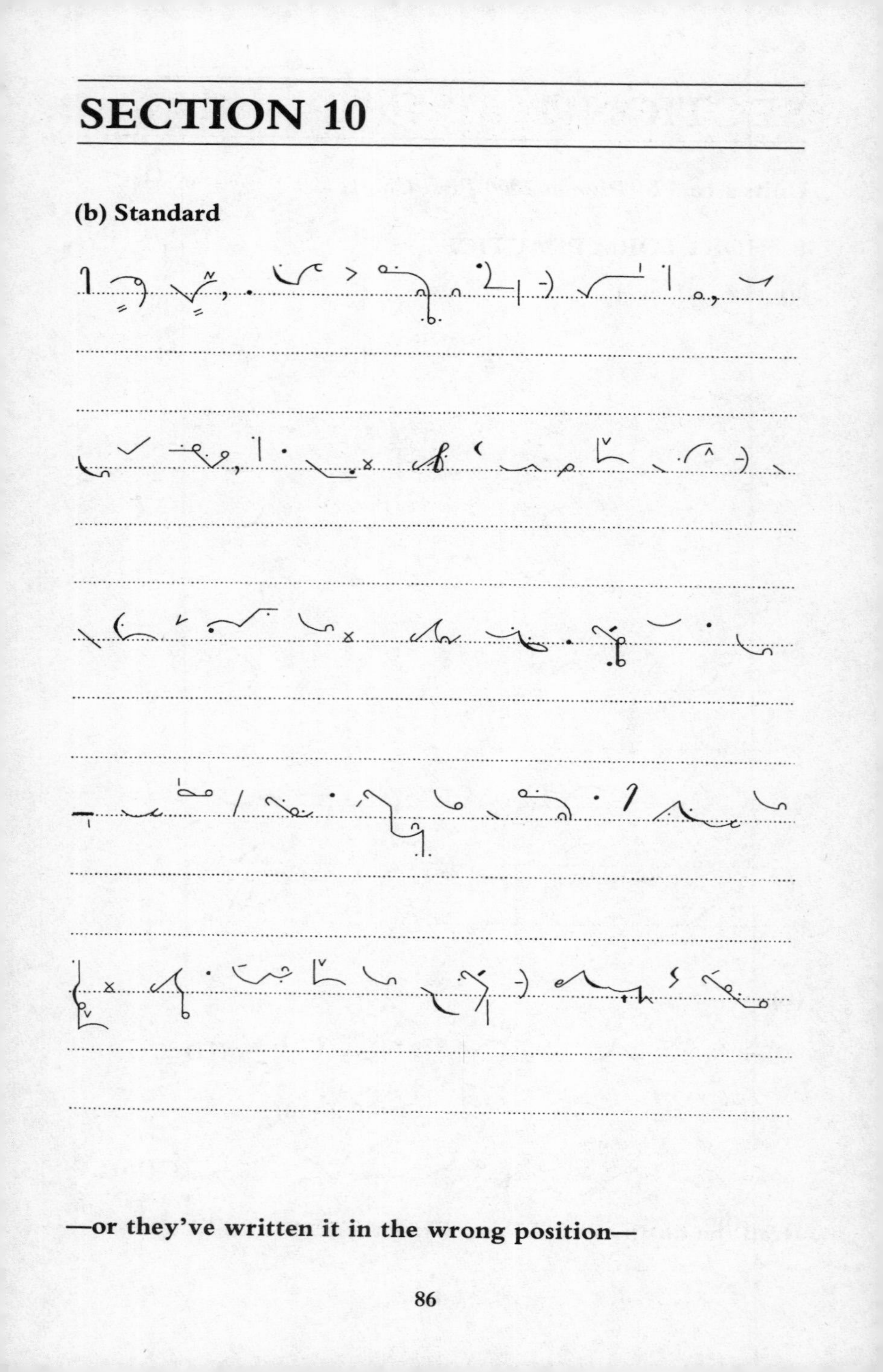

SECTION 10

(b) Standard

—or they've written it in the wrong position—

SECTION 1

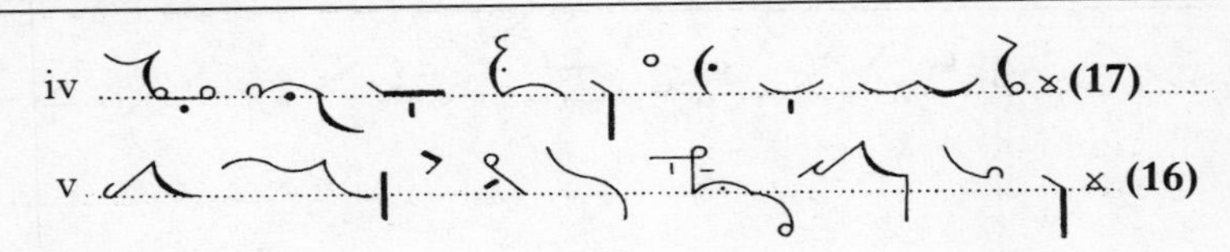

2 PHRASES

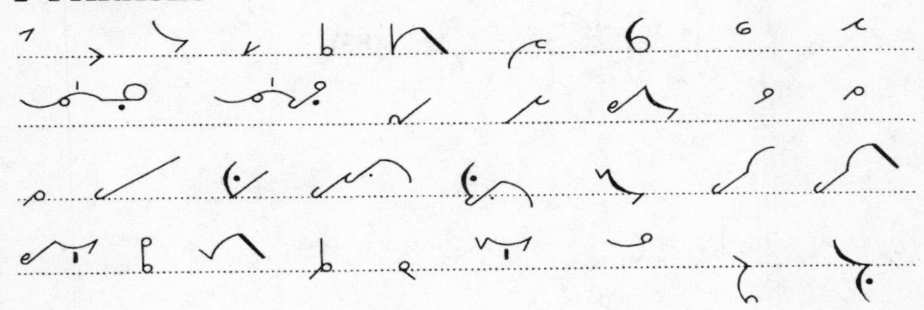

3 DICTATION

(a) Easy

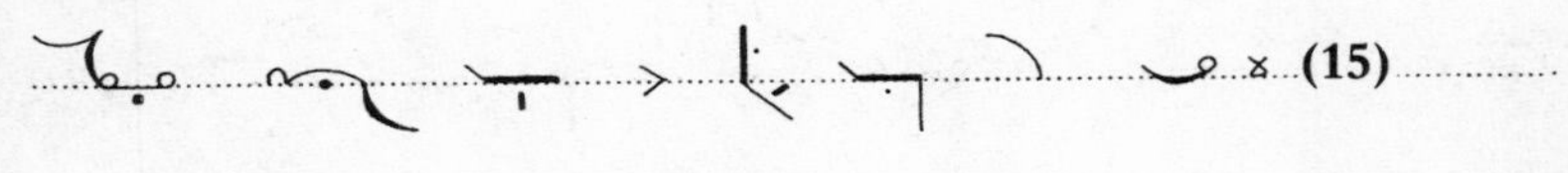

(17)

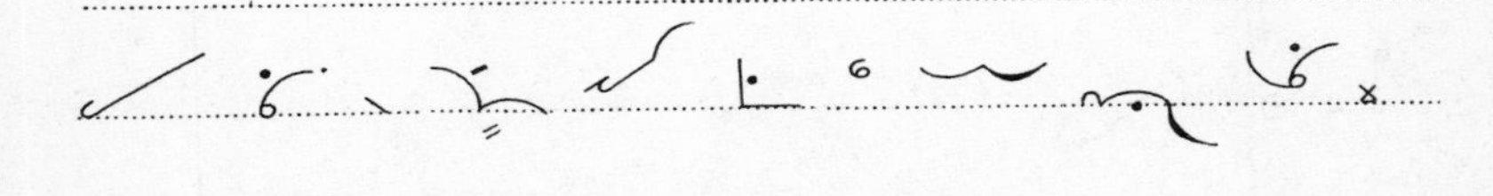

Say the words to yourself while writing the outlines.

SECTION 10

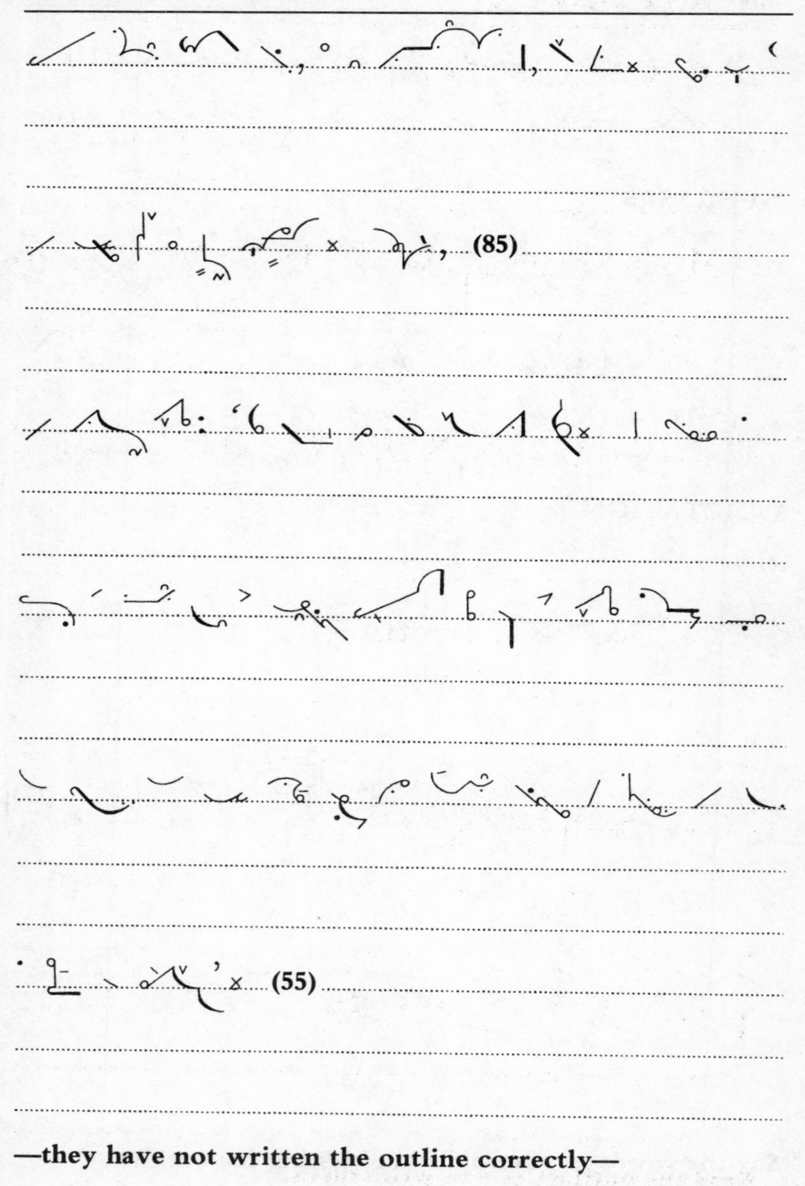

—they have not written the outline correctly—

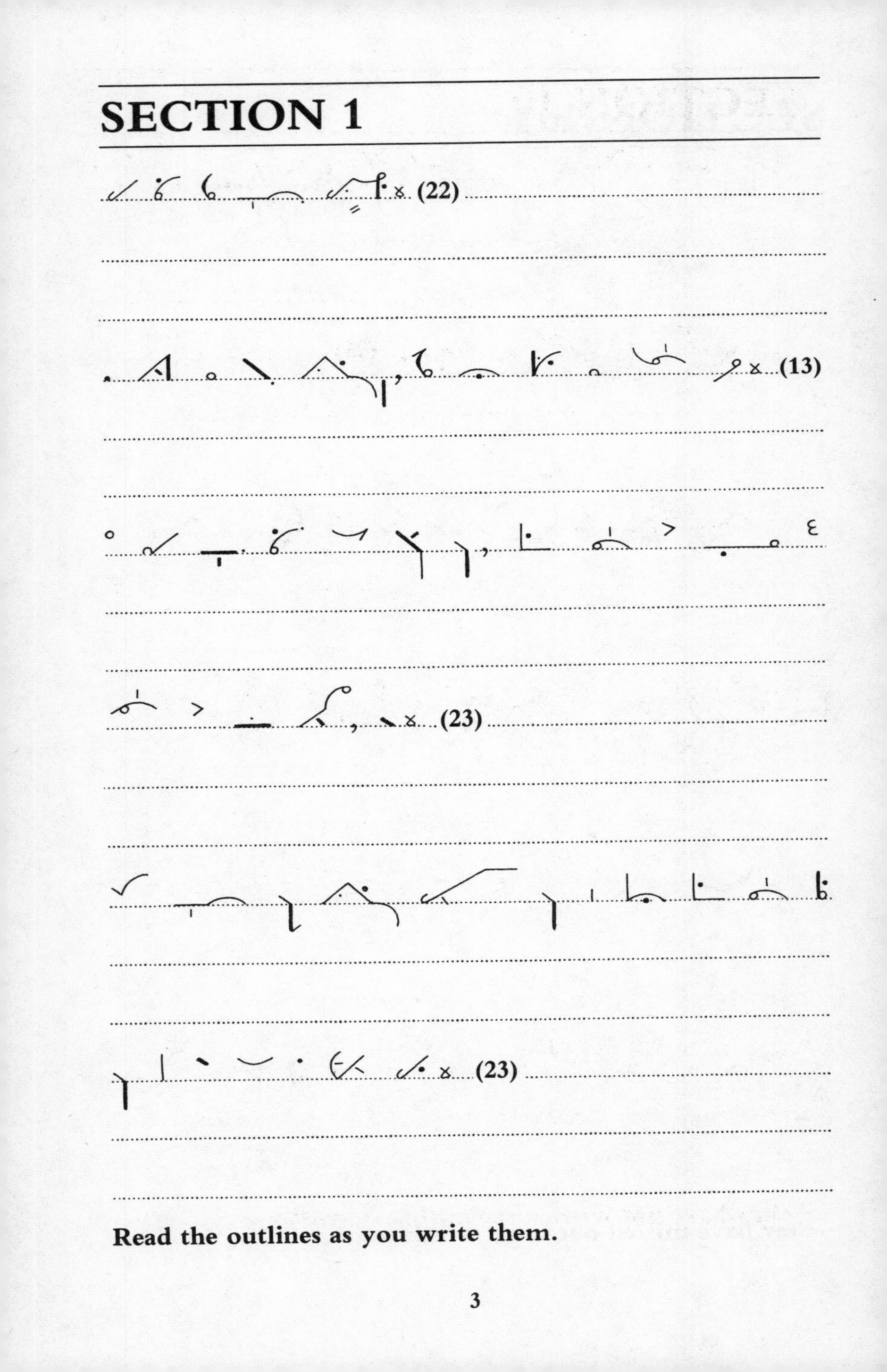

SECTION 1

(22)

(13)

(23)

(23)

Read the outlines as you write them.

SECTION 10

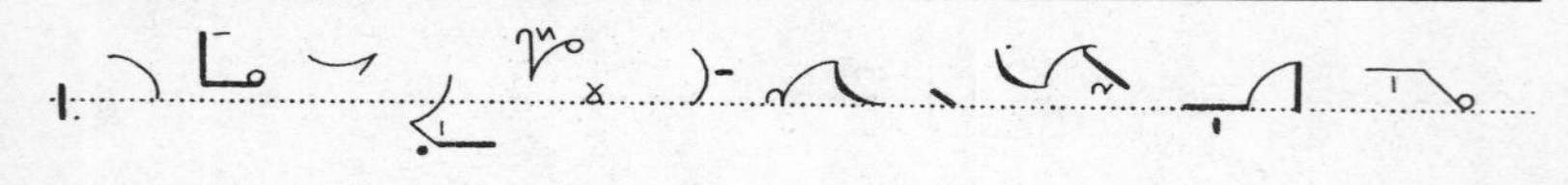

(87)

—they have missed out some words—

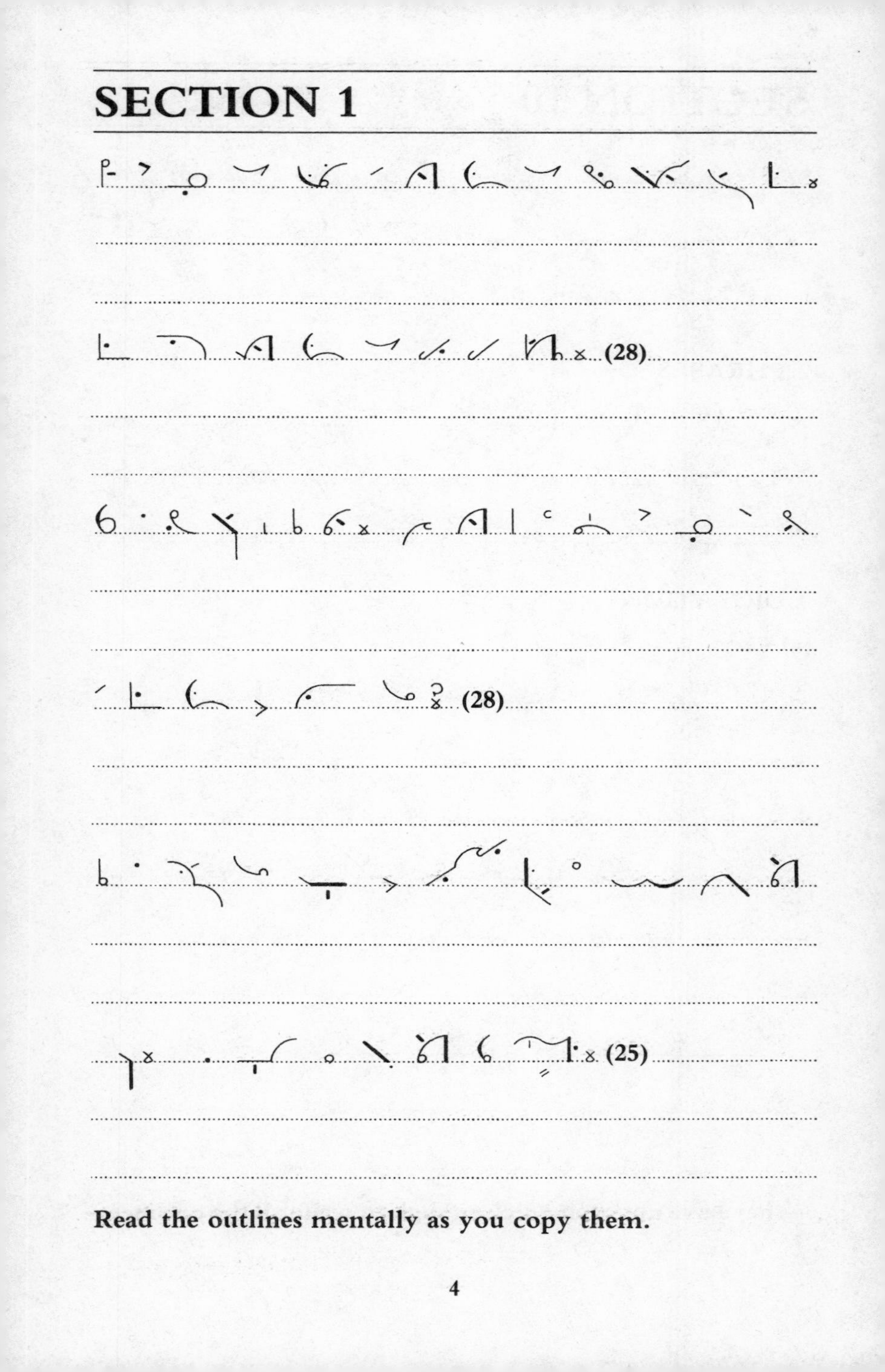

SECTION 1

(28)

(28)

(25)

Read the outlines mentally as you copy them.

SECTION 10

iv

v

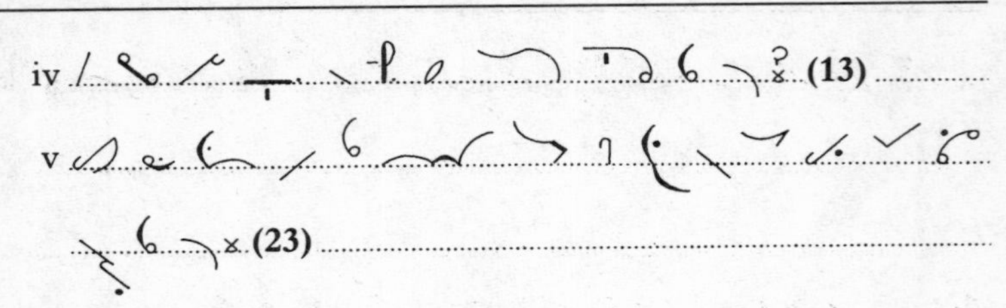

(13)

(23)

2 PHRASES

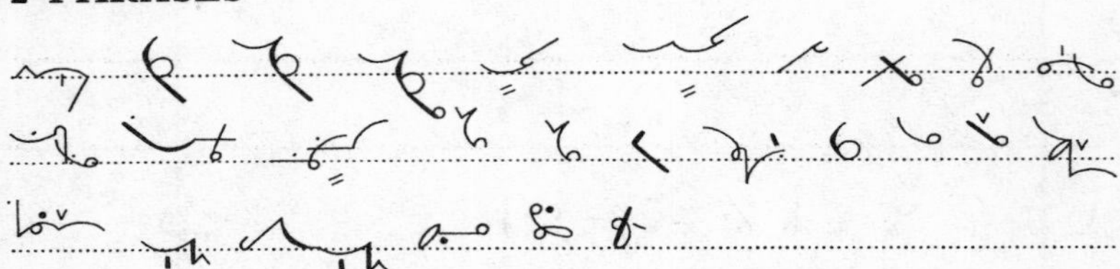

3 DICTATION

(a) Easy

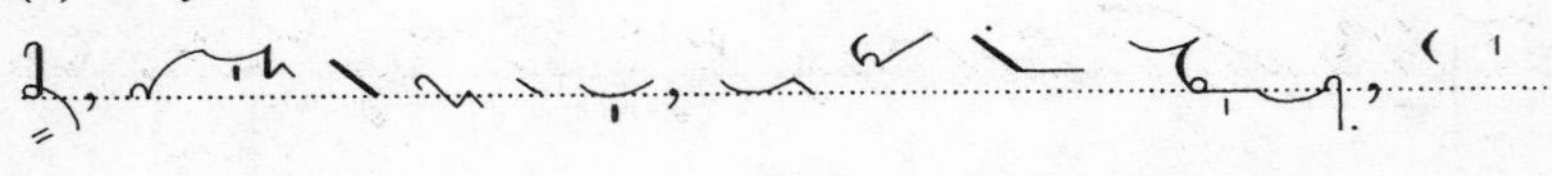

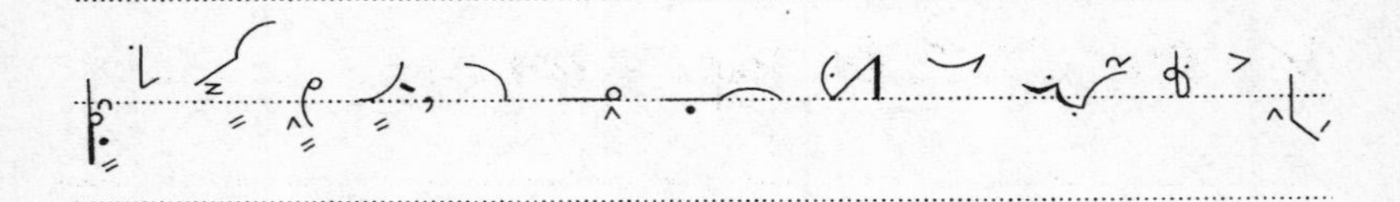

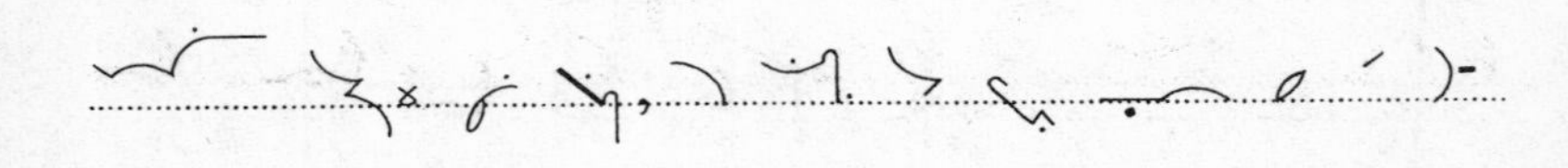

—they have not been quick enough to write all the outlines—

SECTION 1

(29)

(b) Standard

(29)

Write your outlines very lightly.

SECTION 10

Unit 14 of *Pitman 2000 First Course*

1 SHORT FORM PRACTICE

(a)

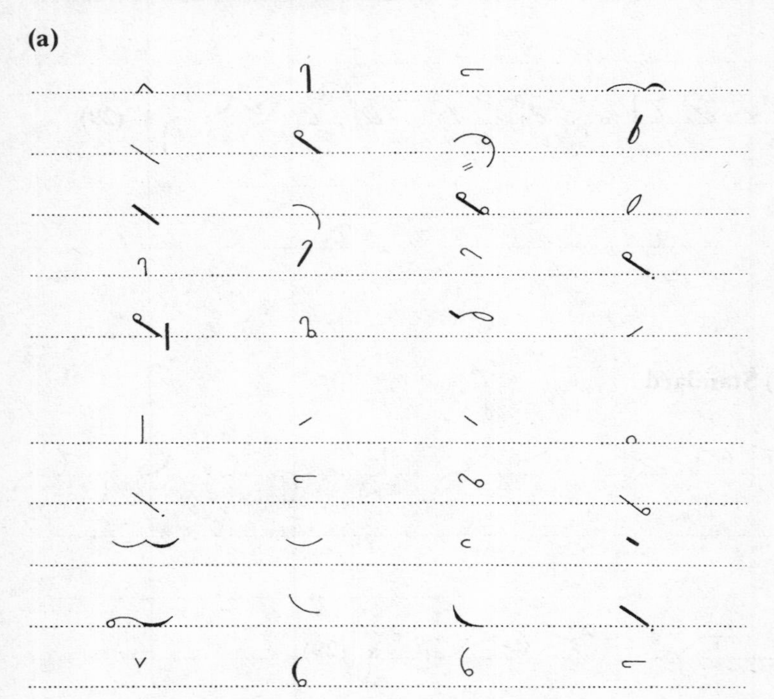

(b)

i (13)

ii (14)

iii (16)

Some reasons why people cannot read their notes are:

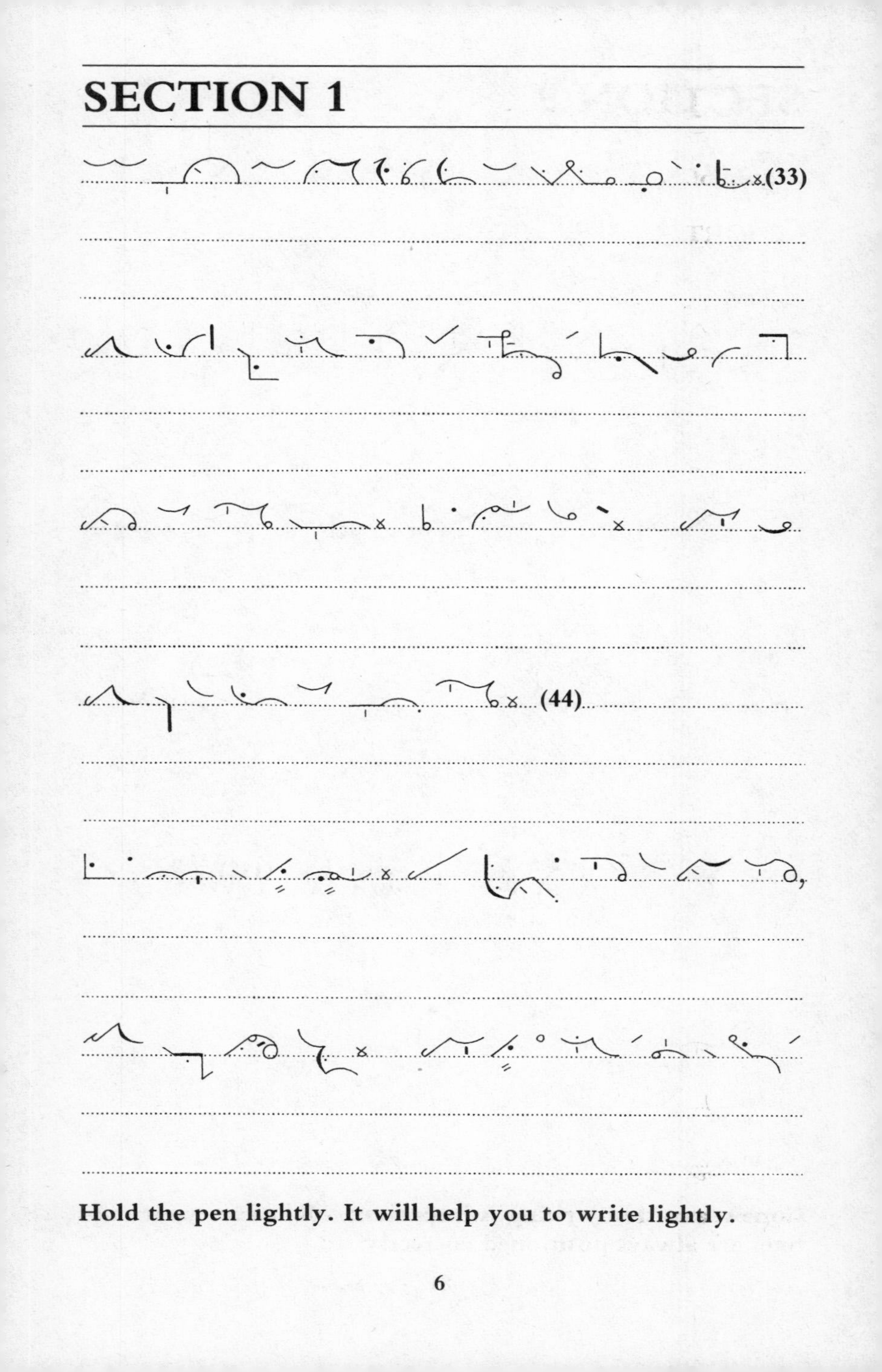

SECTION 1

(33)

(44)

Hold the pen lightly. It will help you to write lightly.

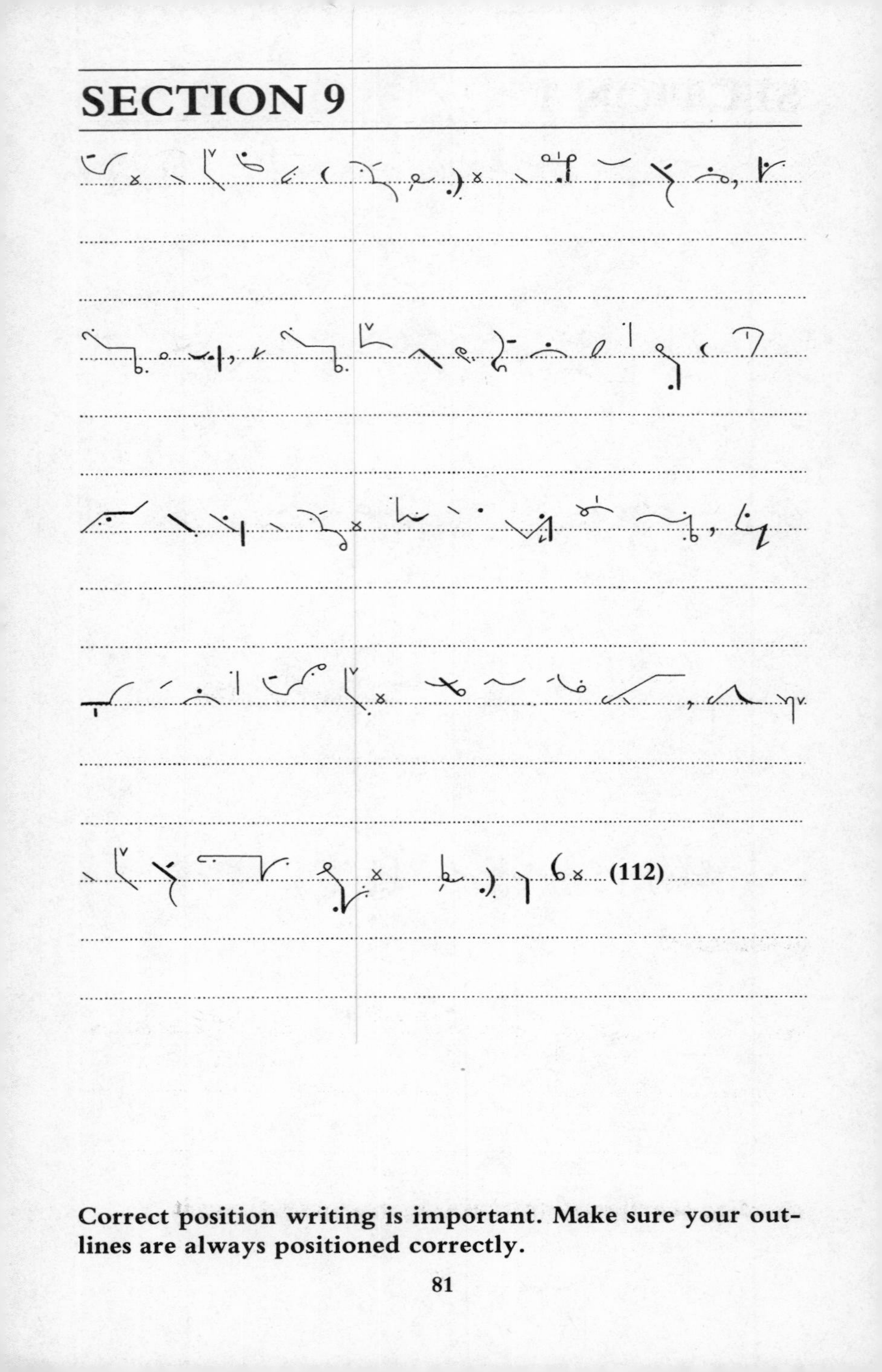

SECTION 9

(112)

Correct position writing is important. Make sure your outlines are always positioned correctly.

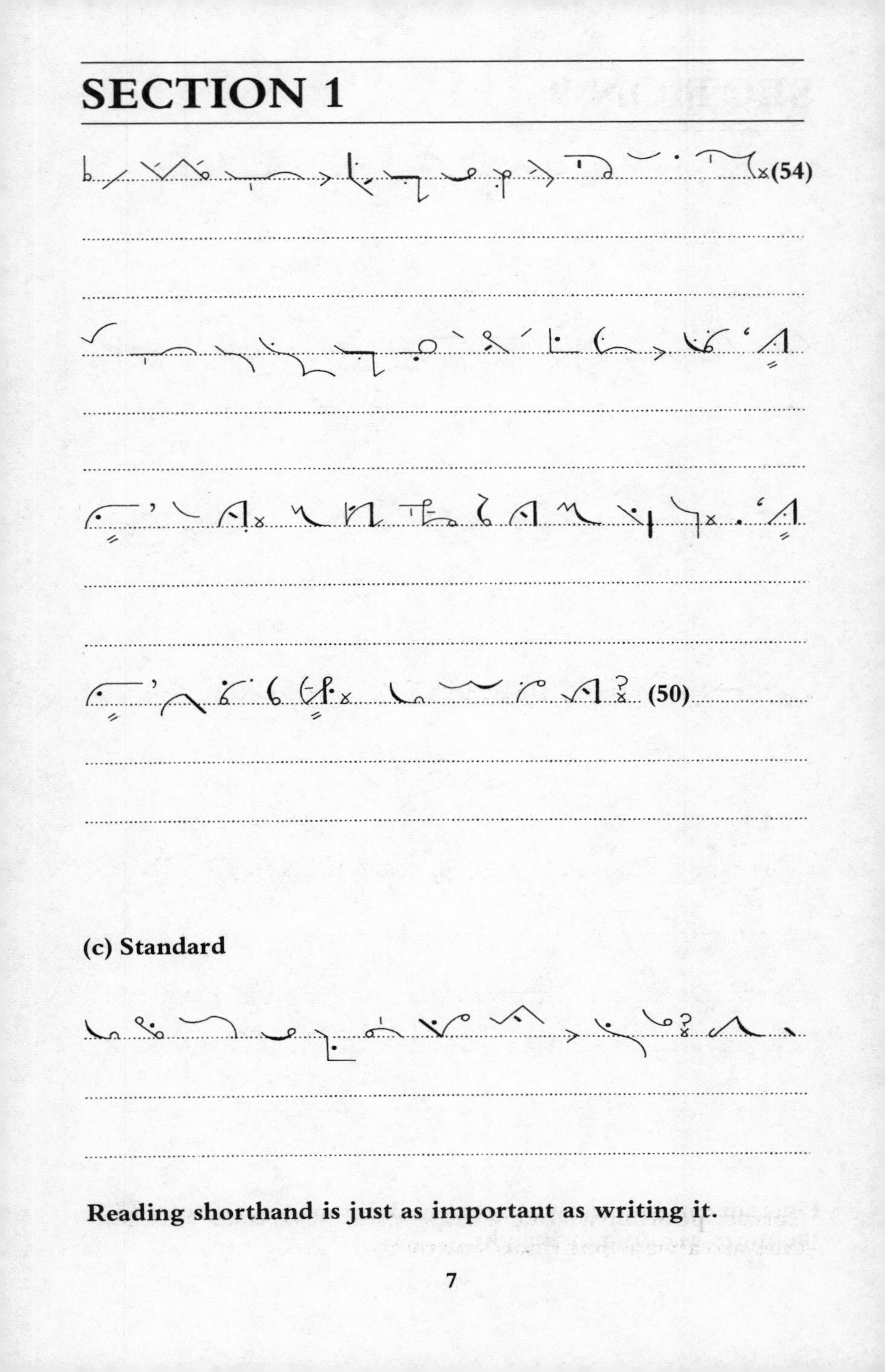

SECTION 1

(54)

(50)

(c) Standard

Reading shorthand is just as important as writing it.

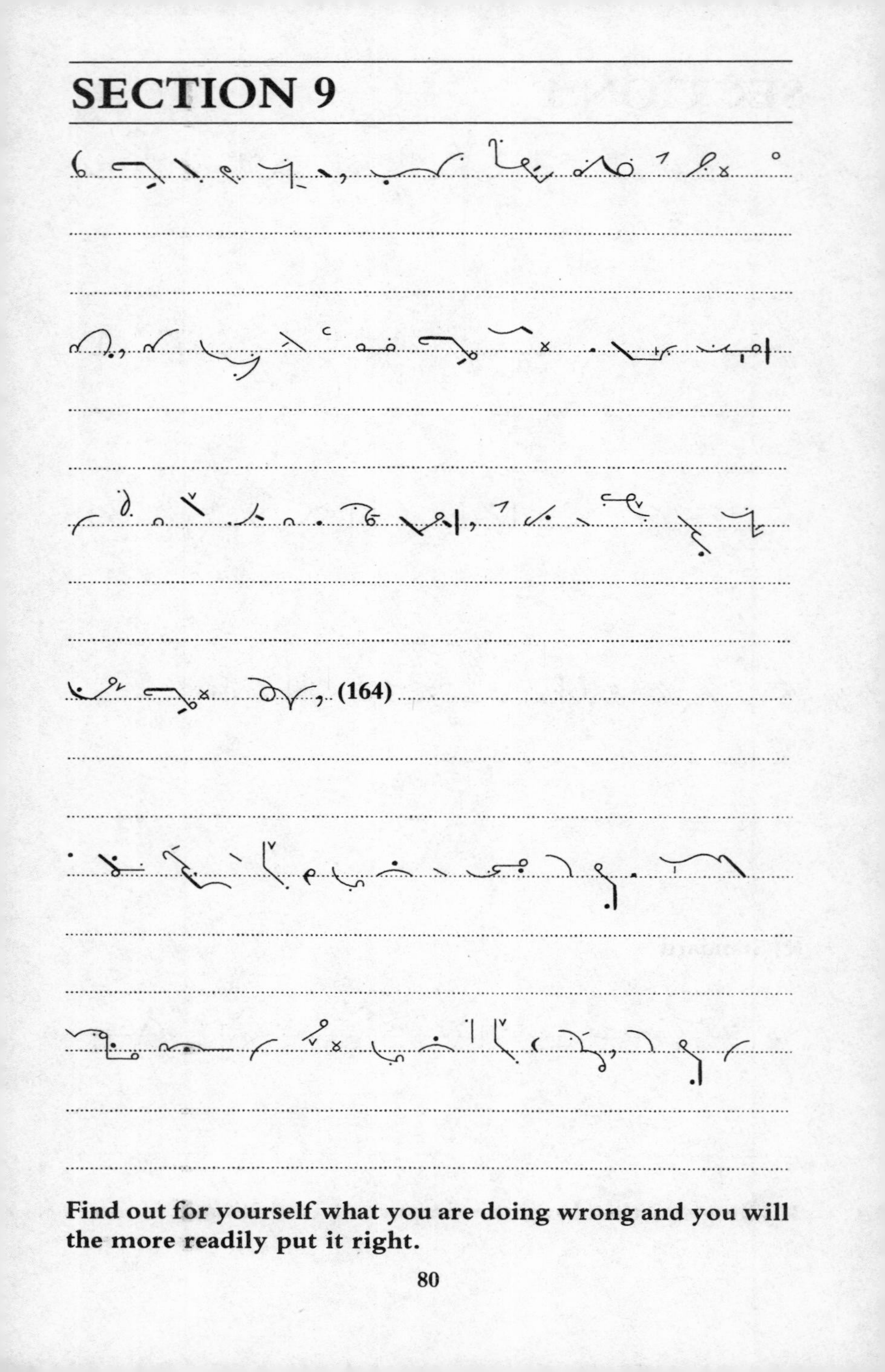

SECTION 9

(164)

Find out for yourself what you are doing wrong and you will the more readily put it right.

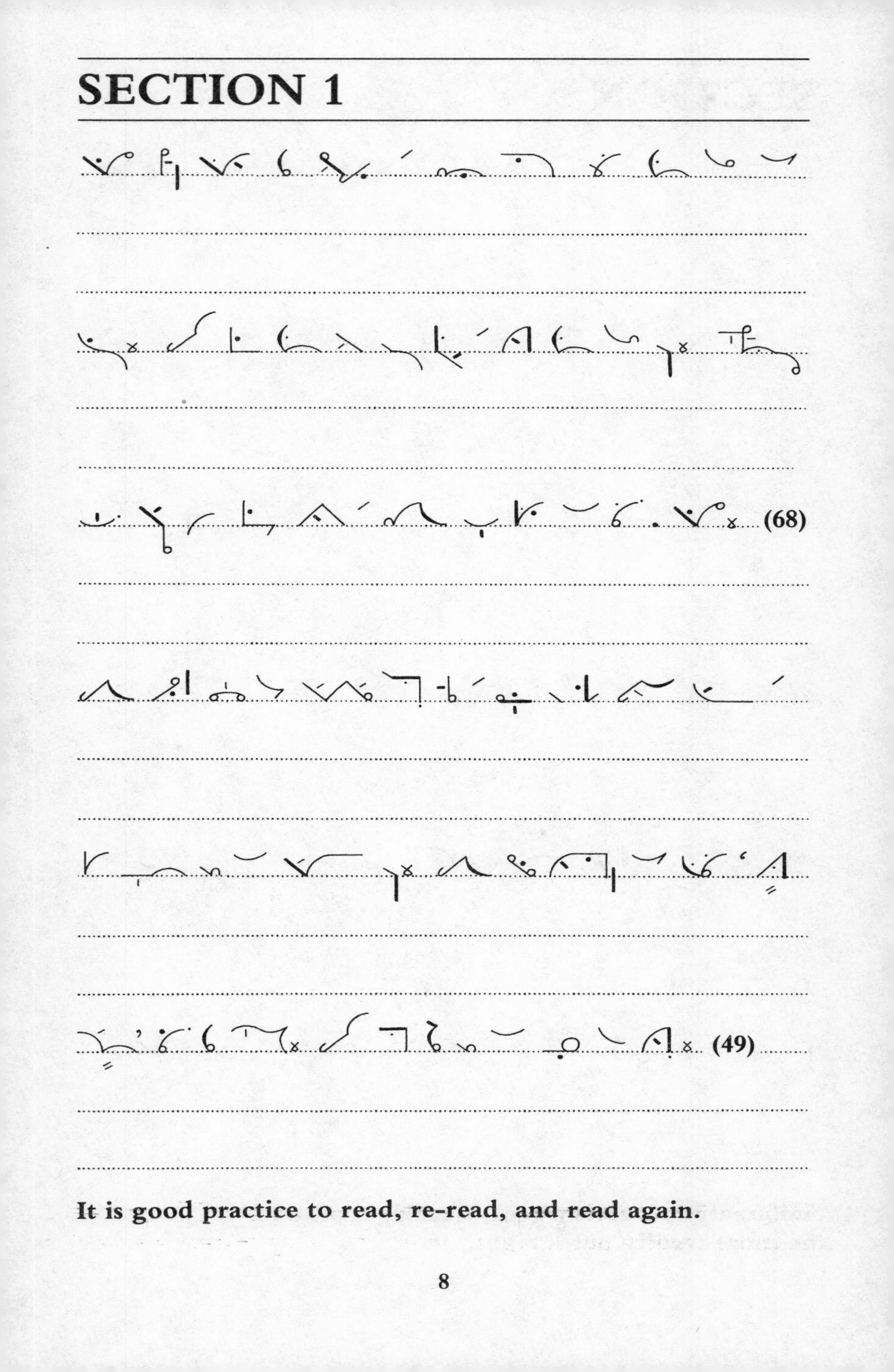

SECTION 1

(68)

(49)

It is good practice to read, re-read, and read again.

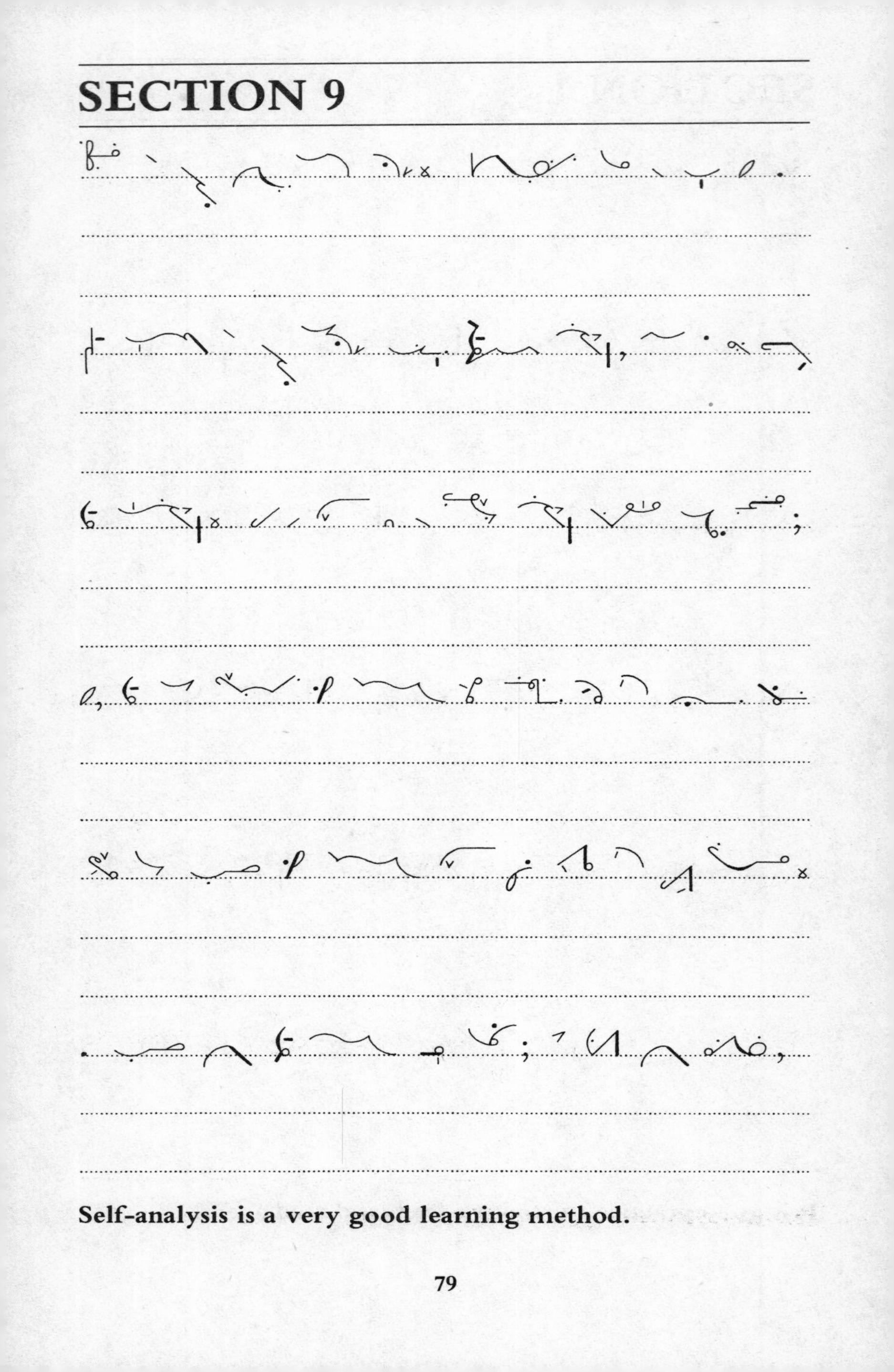

SECTION 9

Self-analysis is a very good learning method.

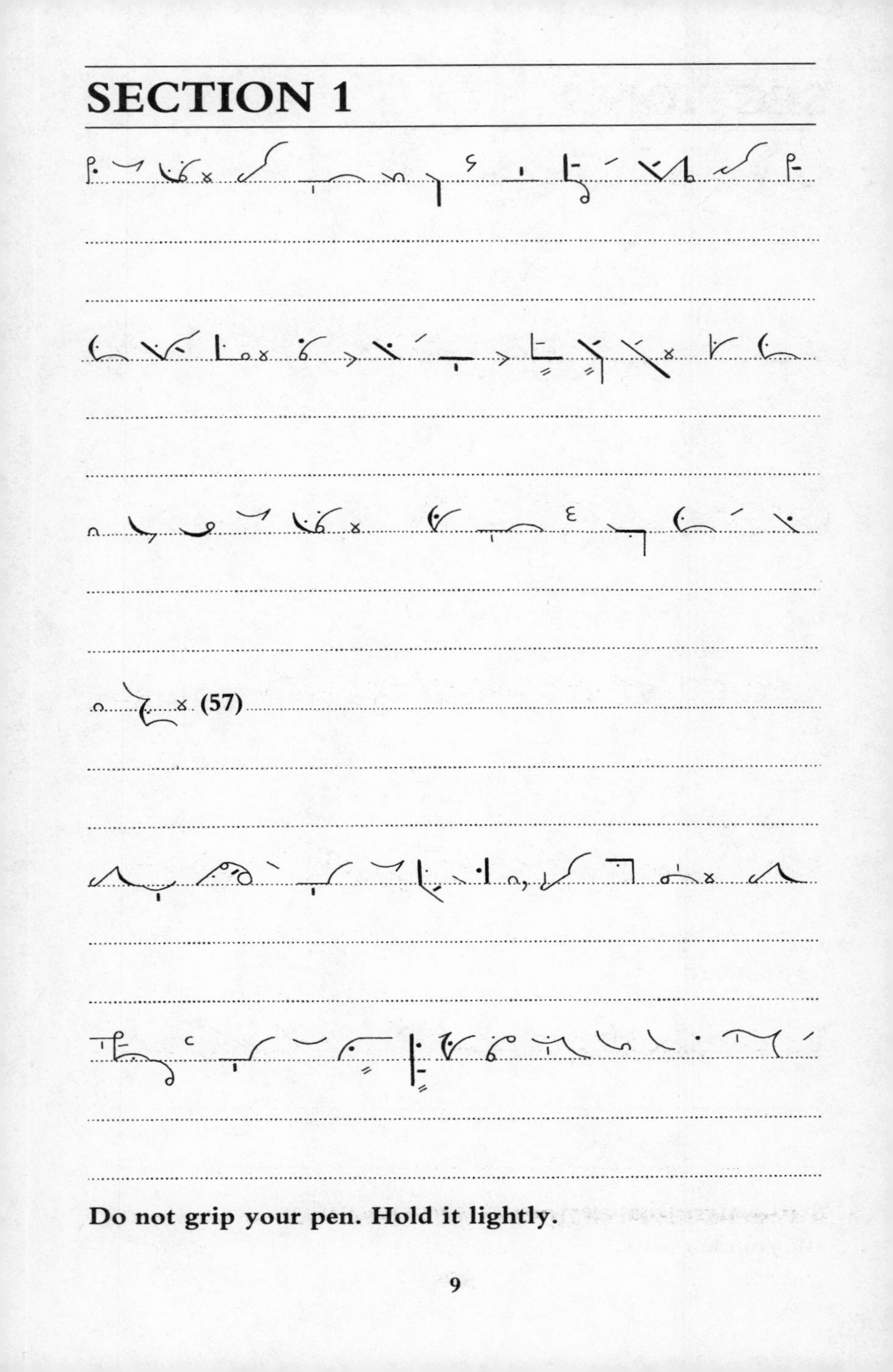

SECTION 1

(57)

Do not grip your pen. Hold it lightly.

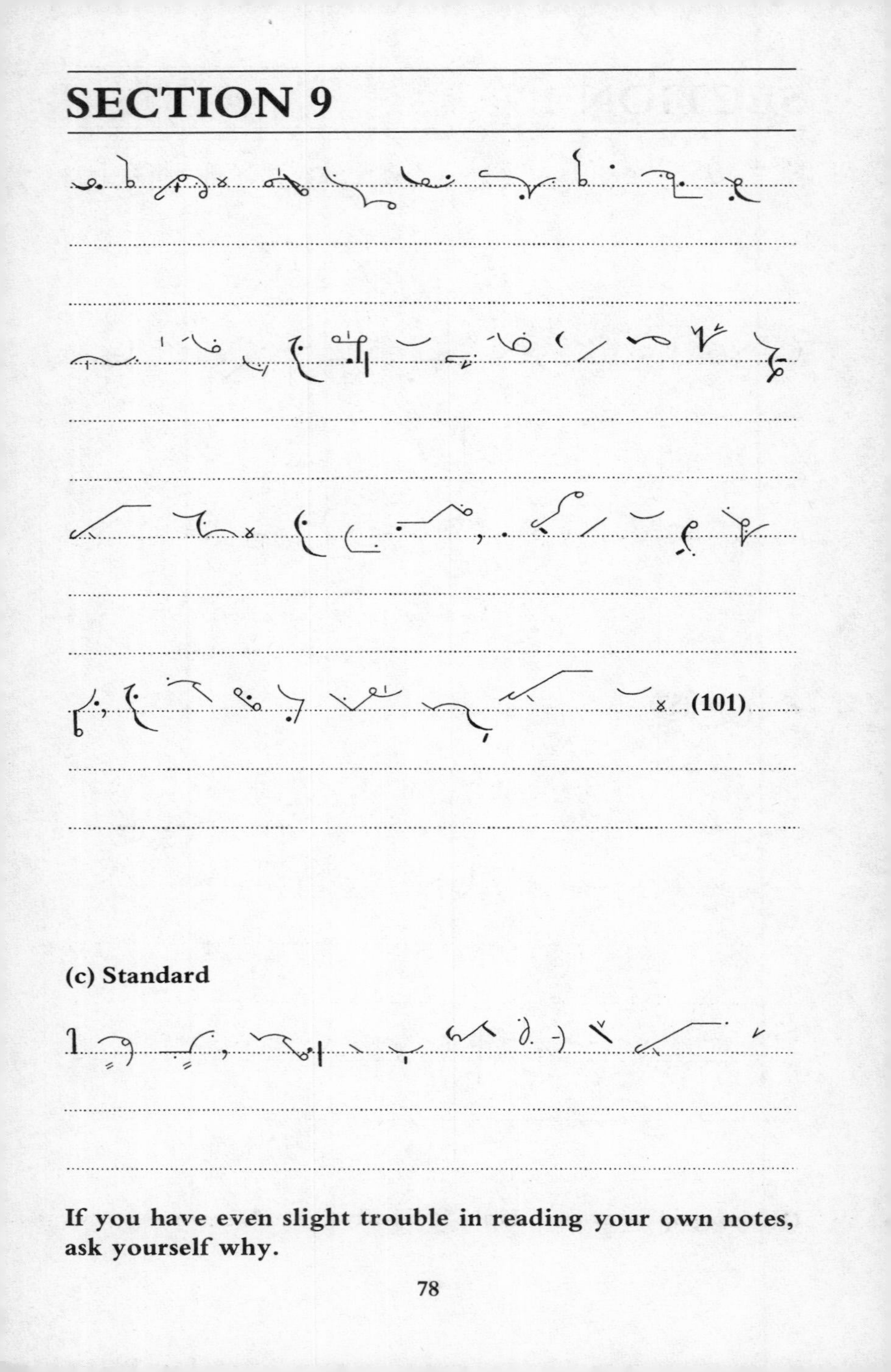

SECTION 9

(101)

(c) Standard

If you have even slight trouble in reading your own notes, ask yourself why.

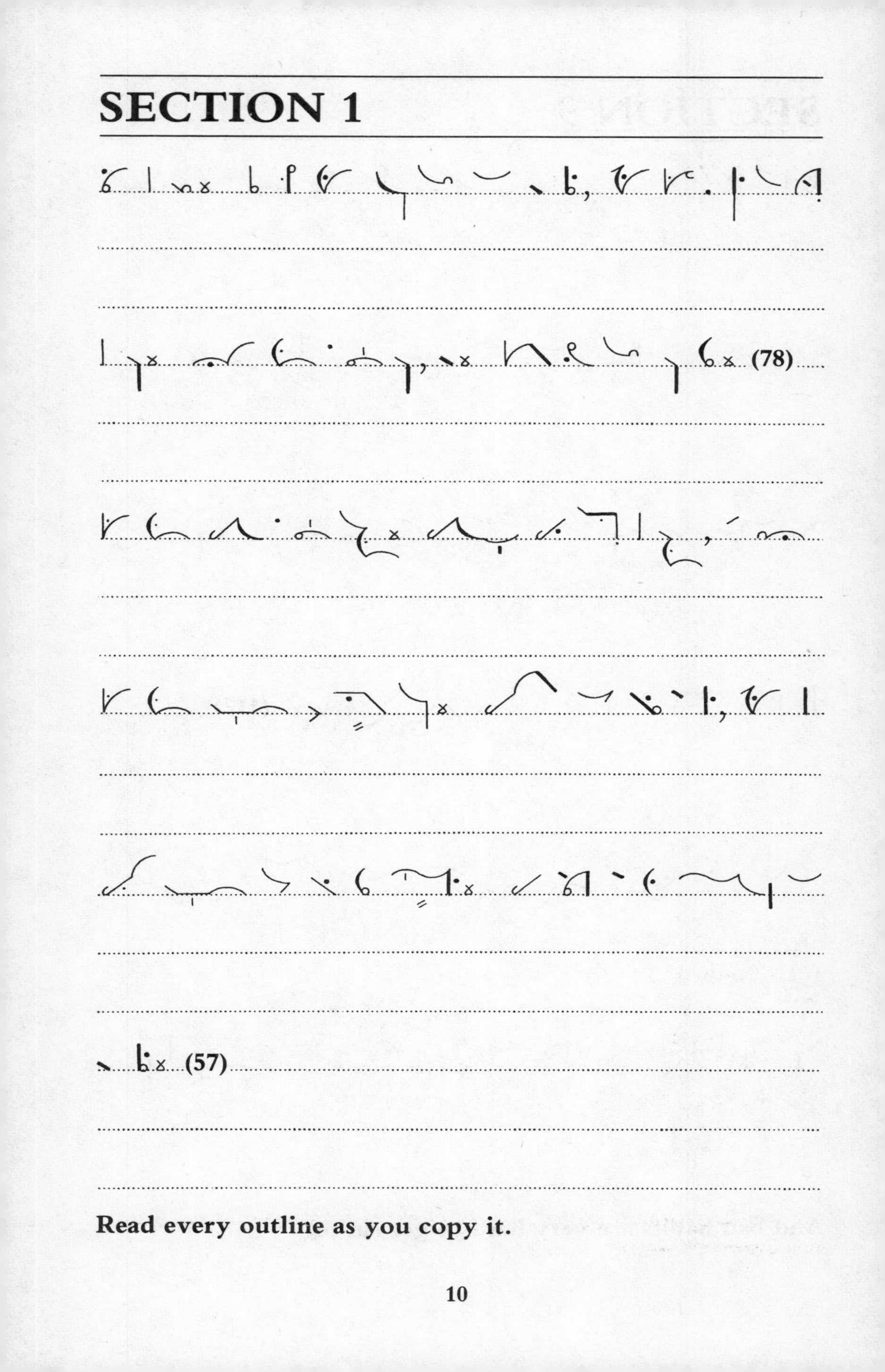

SECTION 1

(78)

(57)

Read every outline as you copy it.

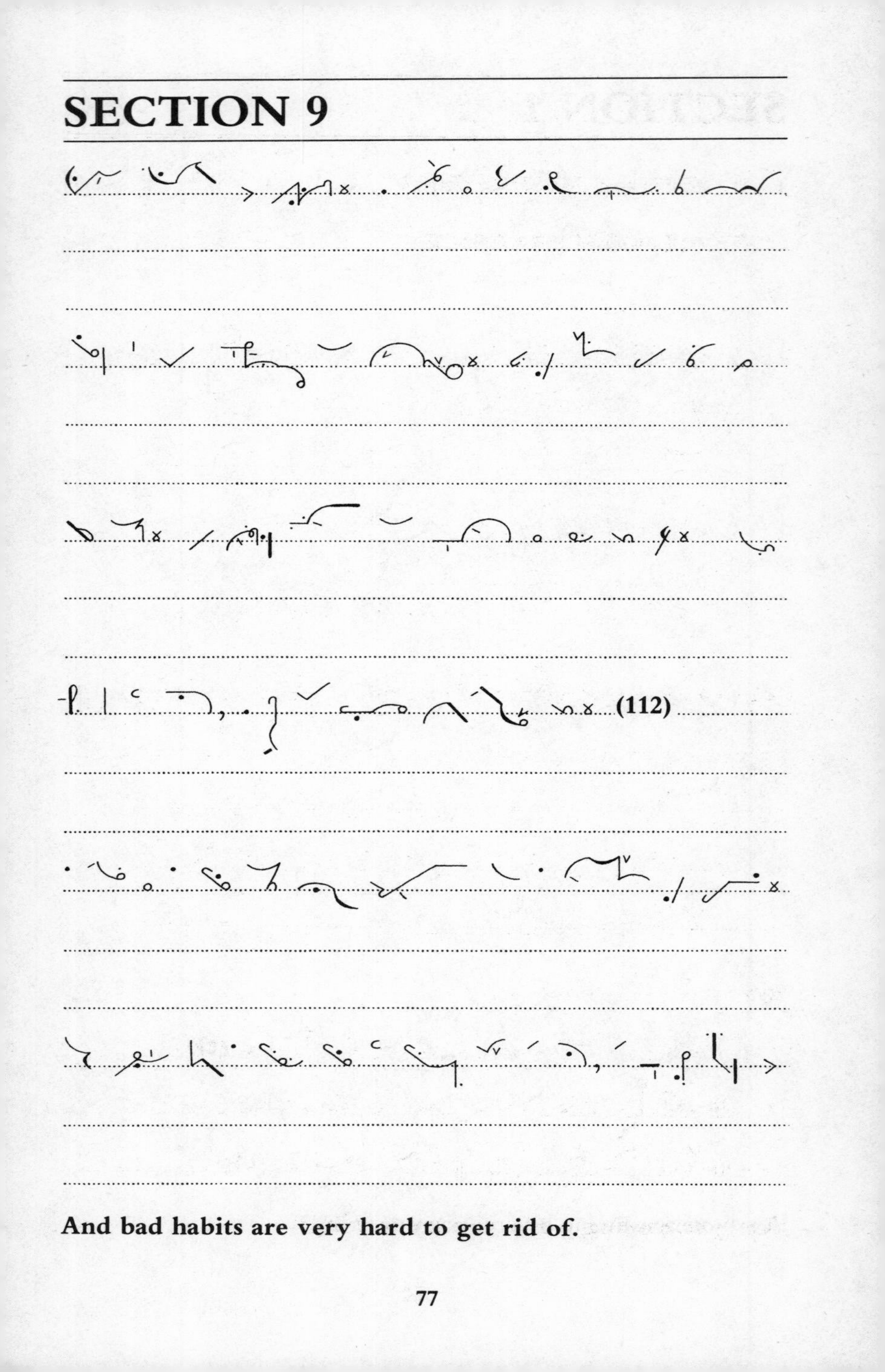

SECTION 9

(112)

And bad habits are very hard to get rid of.

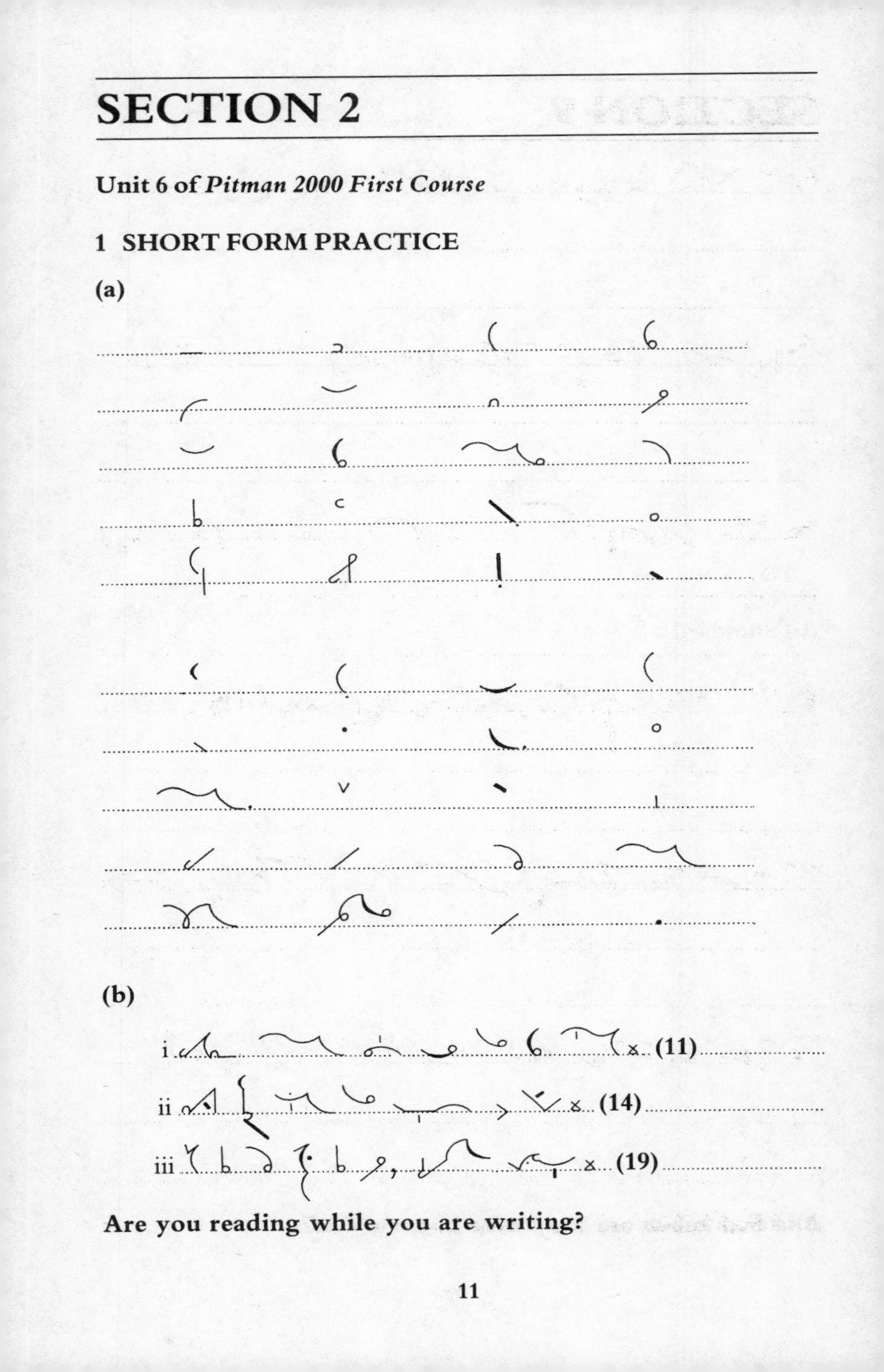

SECTION 2

Unit 6 of *Pitman 2000 First Course*

1 SHORT FORM PRACTICE

(a)

(b)

i (11)

ii (14)

iii (19)

Are you reading while you are writing?

SECTION 9

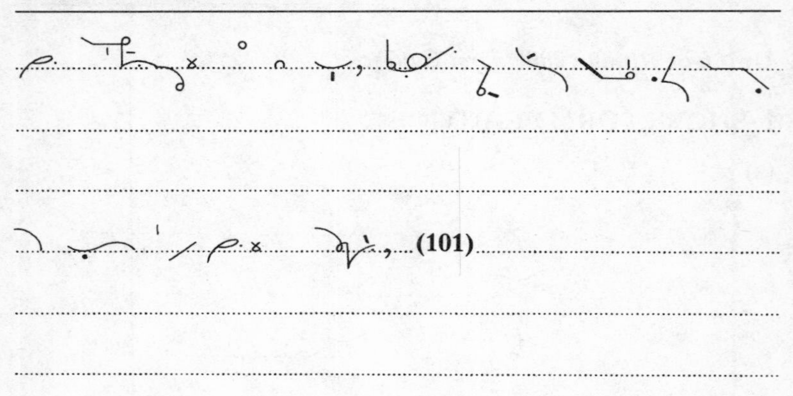

(b) Standard

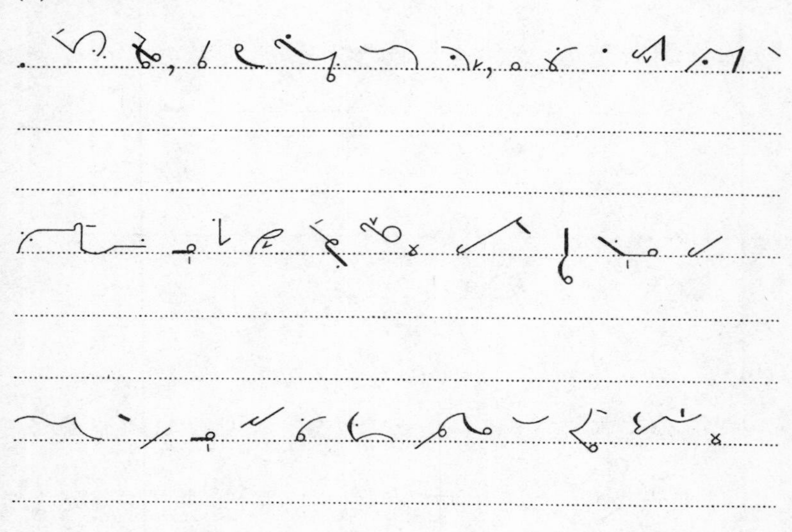

Mistakes made once or twice become a habit.

SECTION 2

iv (18)

v (14)

2 PHRASES

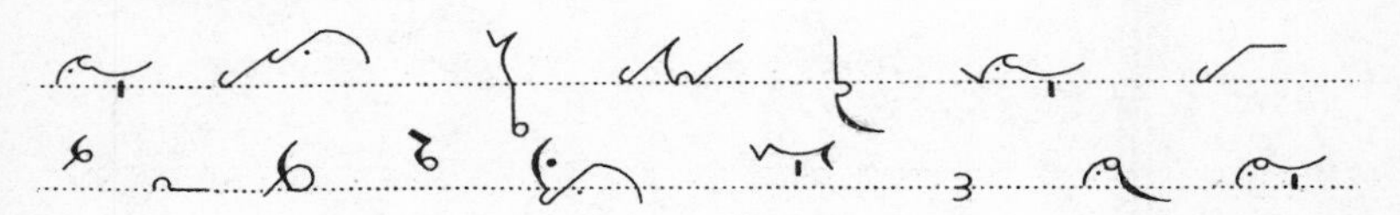

3 DICTATION

(a) Easy

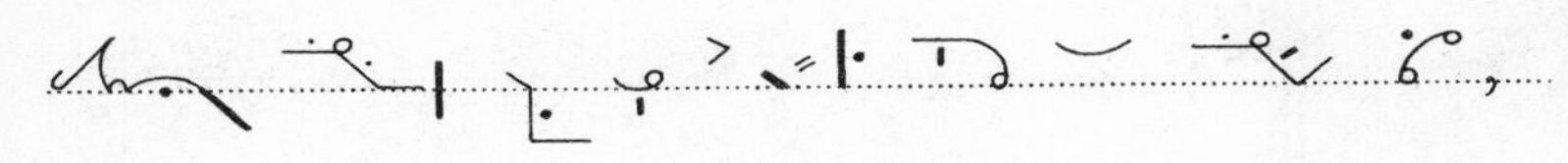

(31)

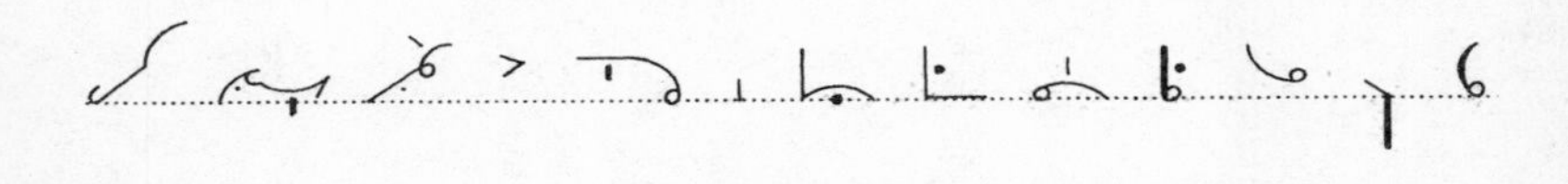

To write shorthand quickly—read shorthand quickly.

SECTION 9

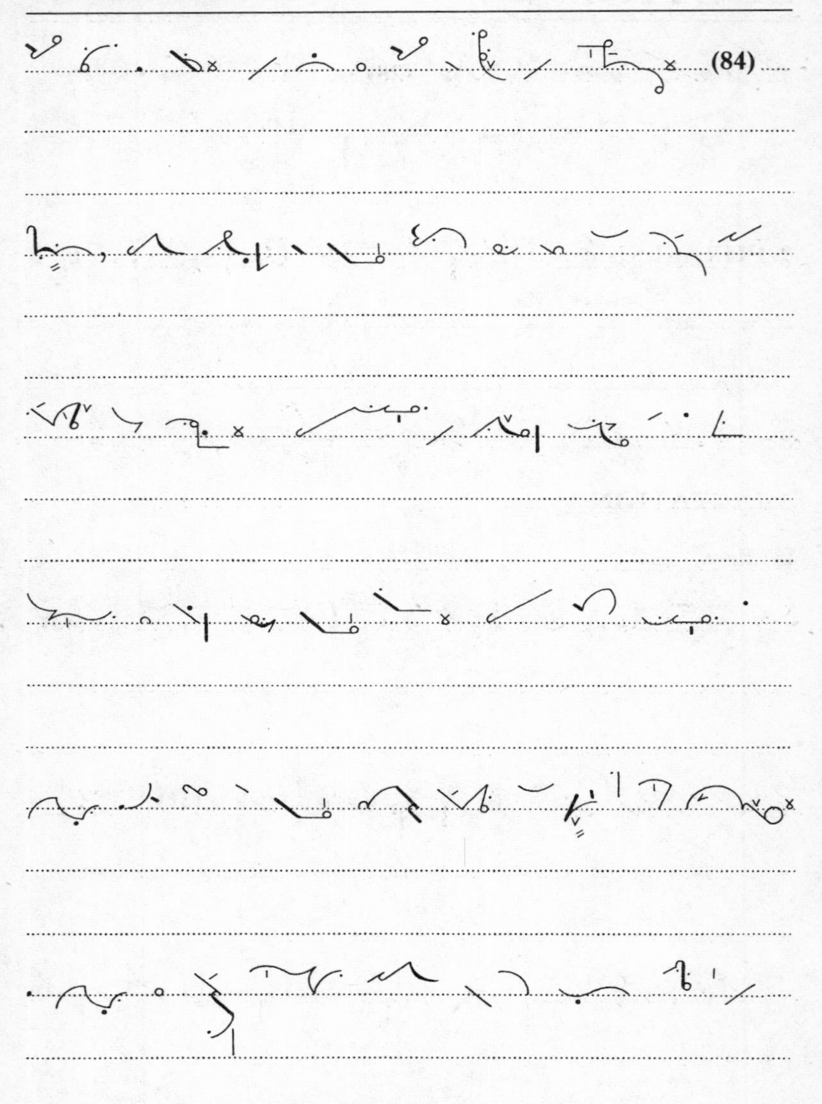

Learn from your mistakes but, even more important, learn not to make mistakes.

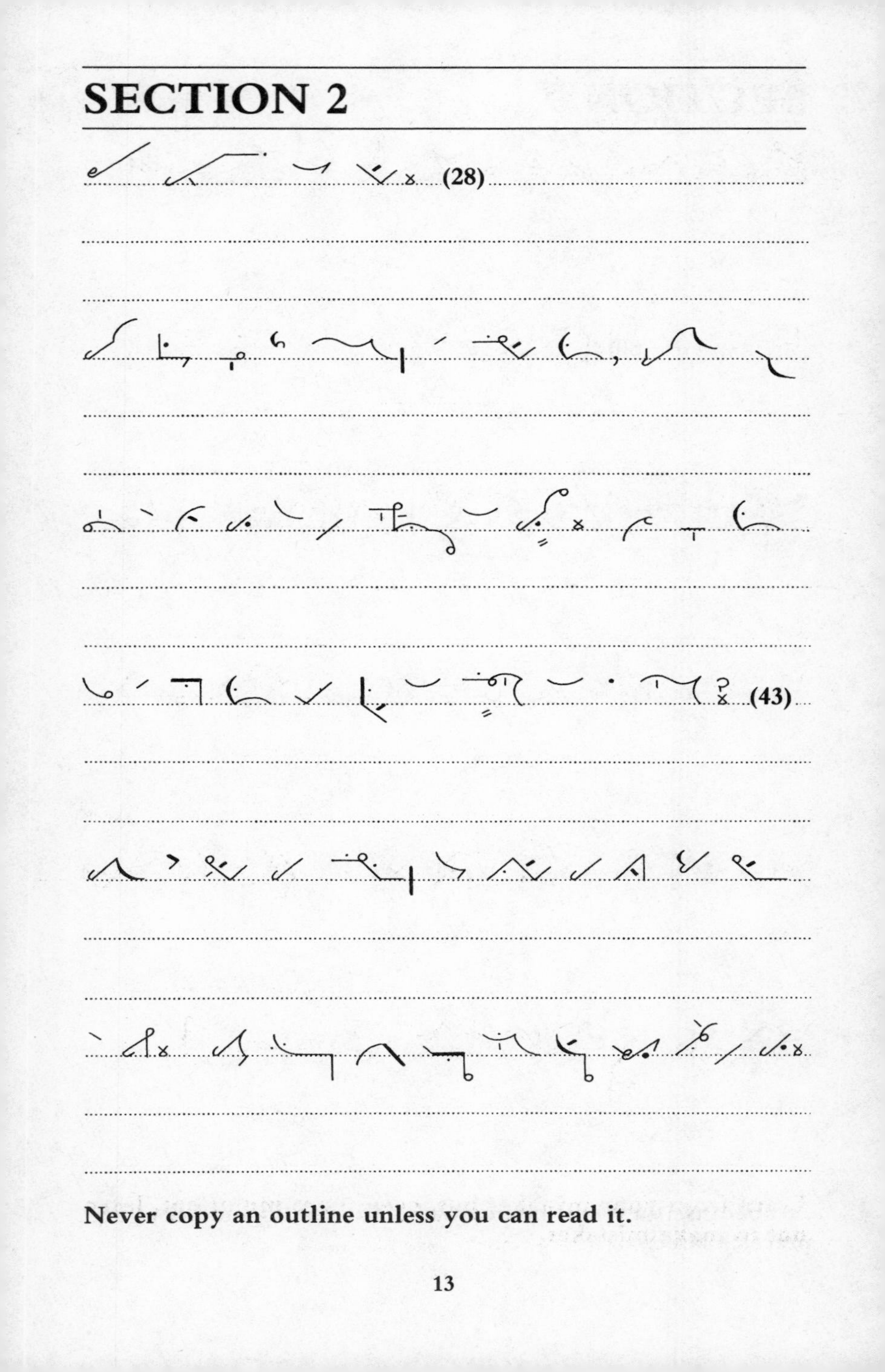

SECTION 2

(28)

(43)

Never copy an outline unless you can read it.

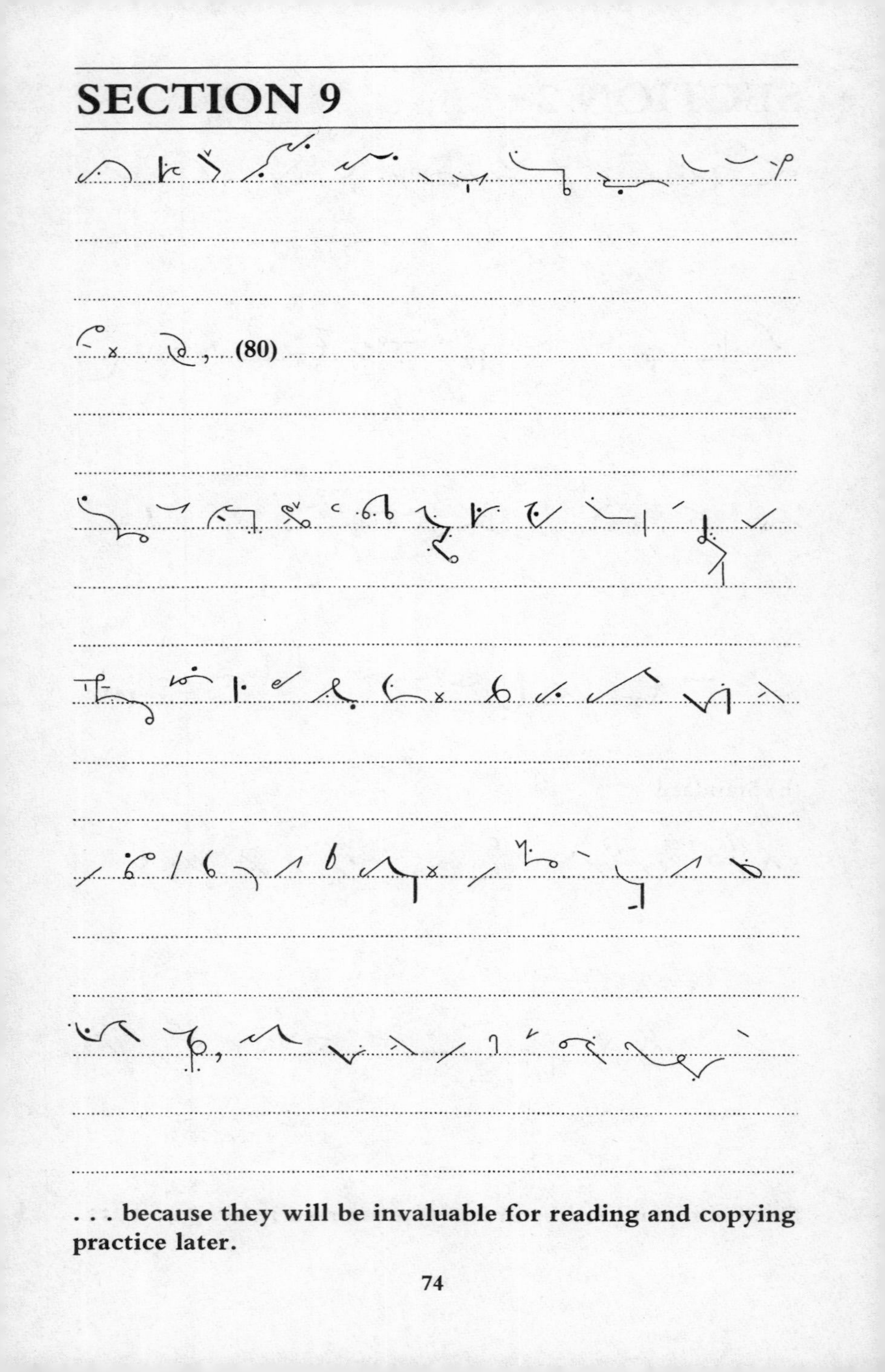

SECTION 9

(80)

. . . **because they will be invaluable for reading and copying practice later.**

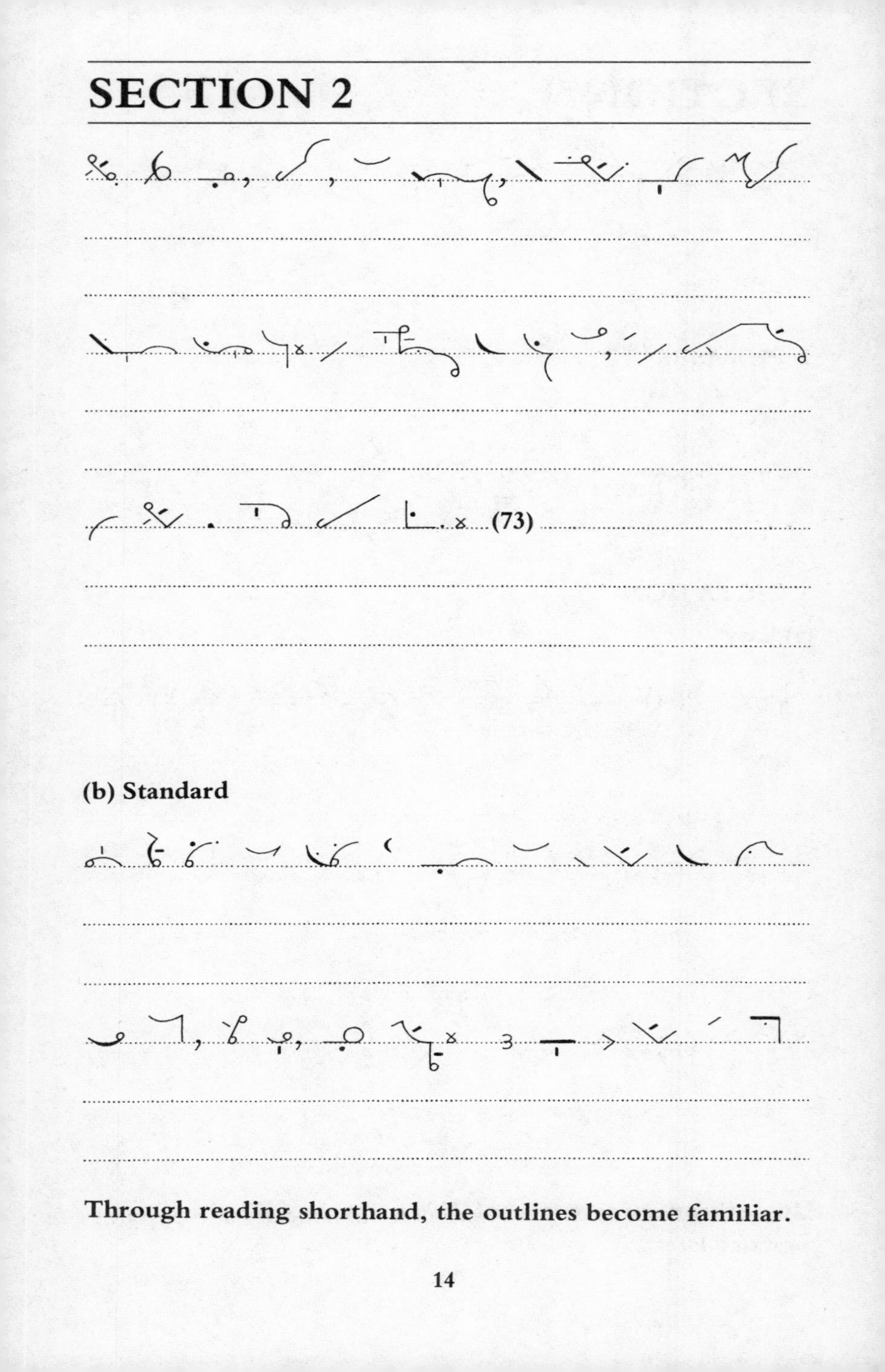

SECTION 2

(73)

(b) Standard

Through reading shorthand, the outlines become familiar.

SECTION 9

iv (23)

v (17)

2 PHRASES

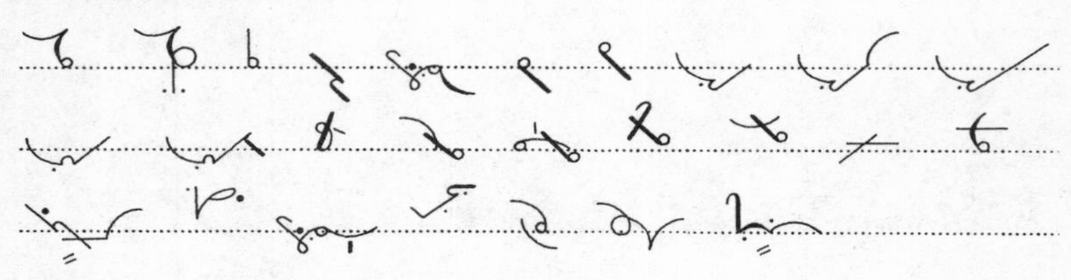

3 DICTATION

(a) Easy

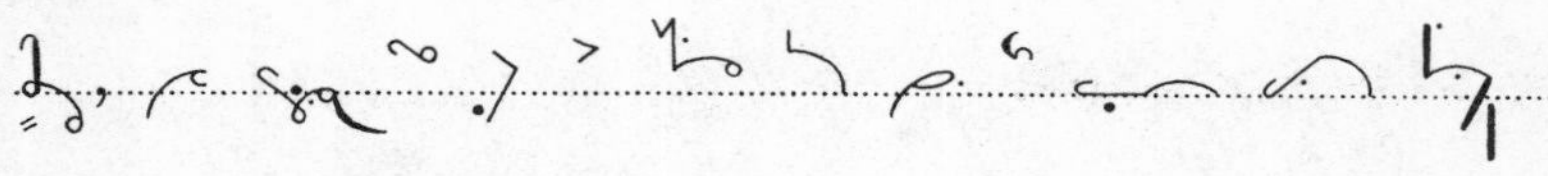

Don't throw away copies of *2000* magazine. Why? . . .

SECTION 2

(89)

Think of the outline as you hear the word.

SECTION 9

Unit 13 of *Pitman 2000 First Course*

1 SHORT FORM PRACTICE

(a)

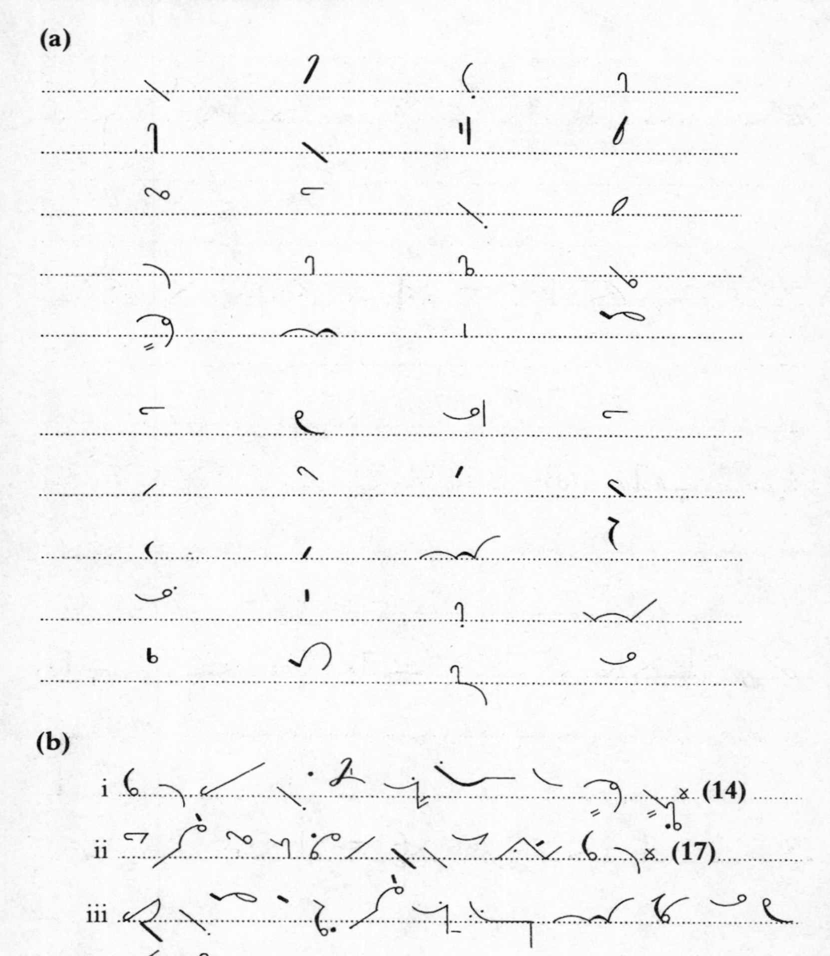

When *not* to phrase is as important as when to phrase.

SECTION 2

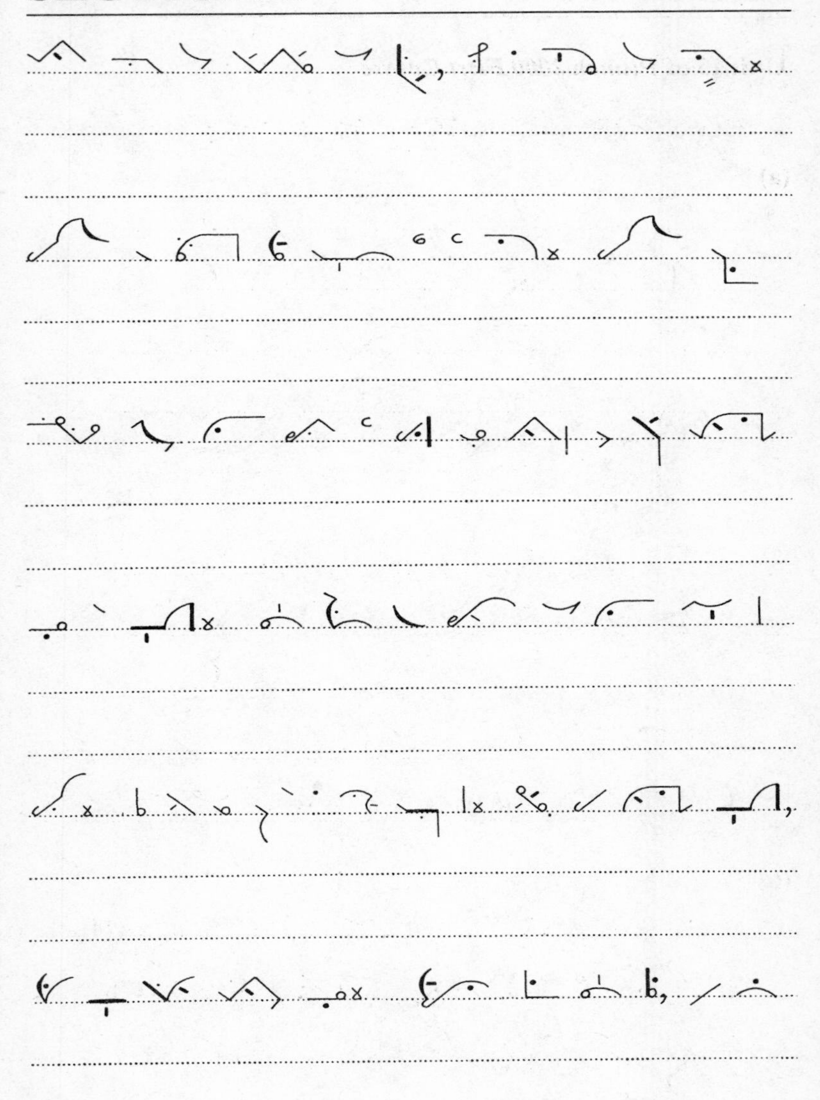

A moment to spare? Re-read the shorthand.

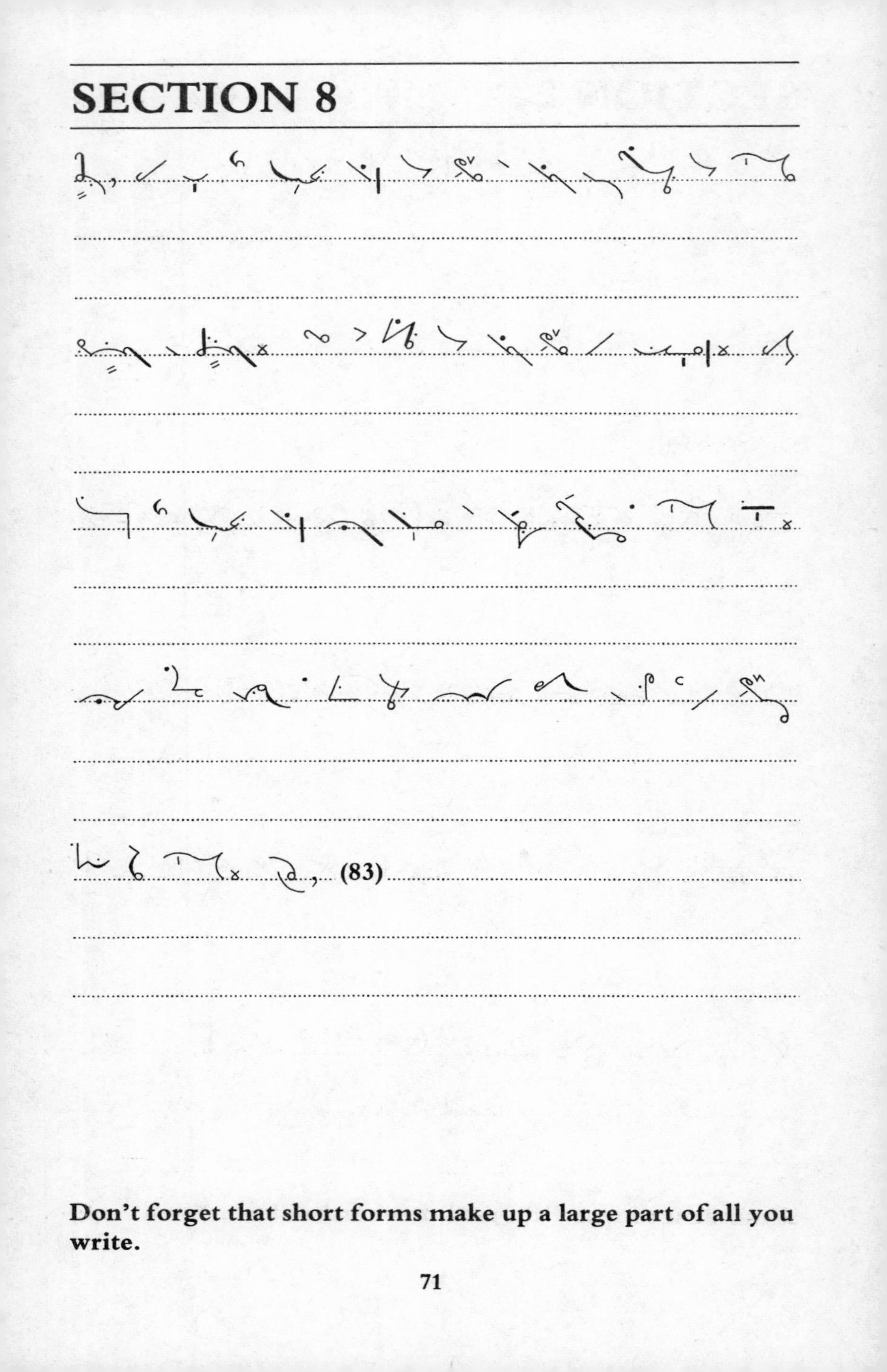

SECTION 8

(83)

Don't forget that short forms make up a large part of all you write.

SECTION 2

(136)

(c) Standard

Hold the notebook firm with your non-writing hand.

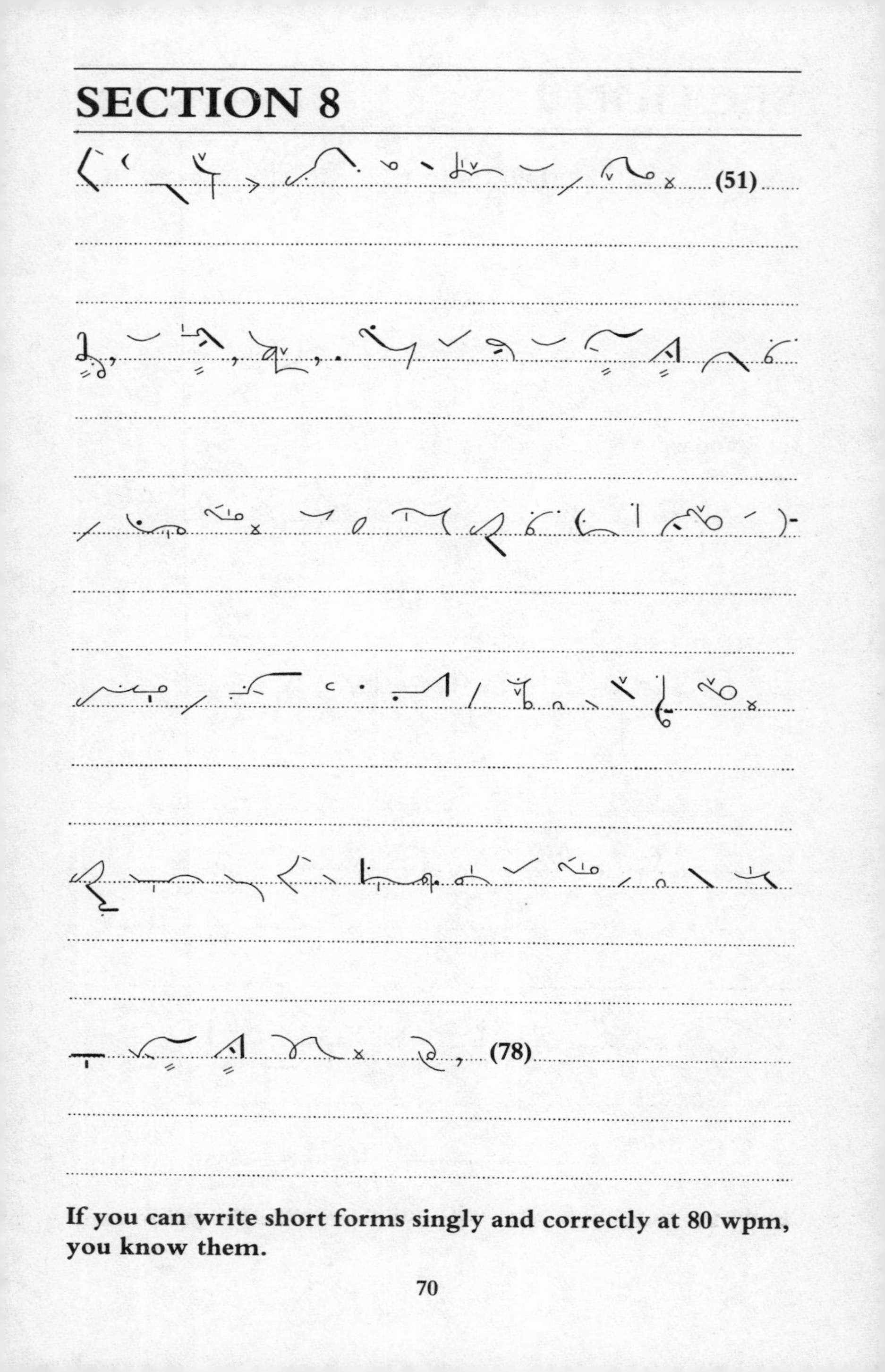

SECTION 8

(51)

(78)

If you can write short forms singly and correctly at 80 wpm, you know them.

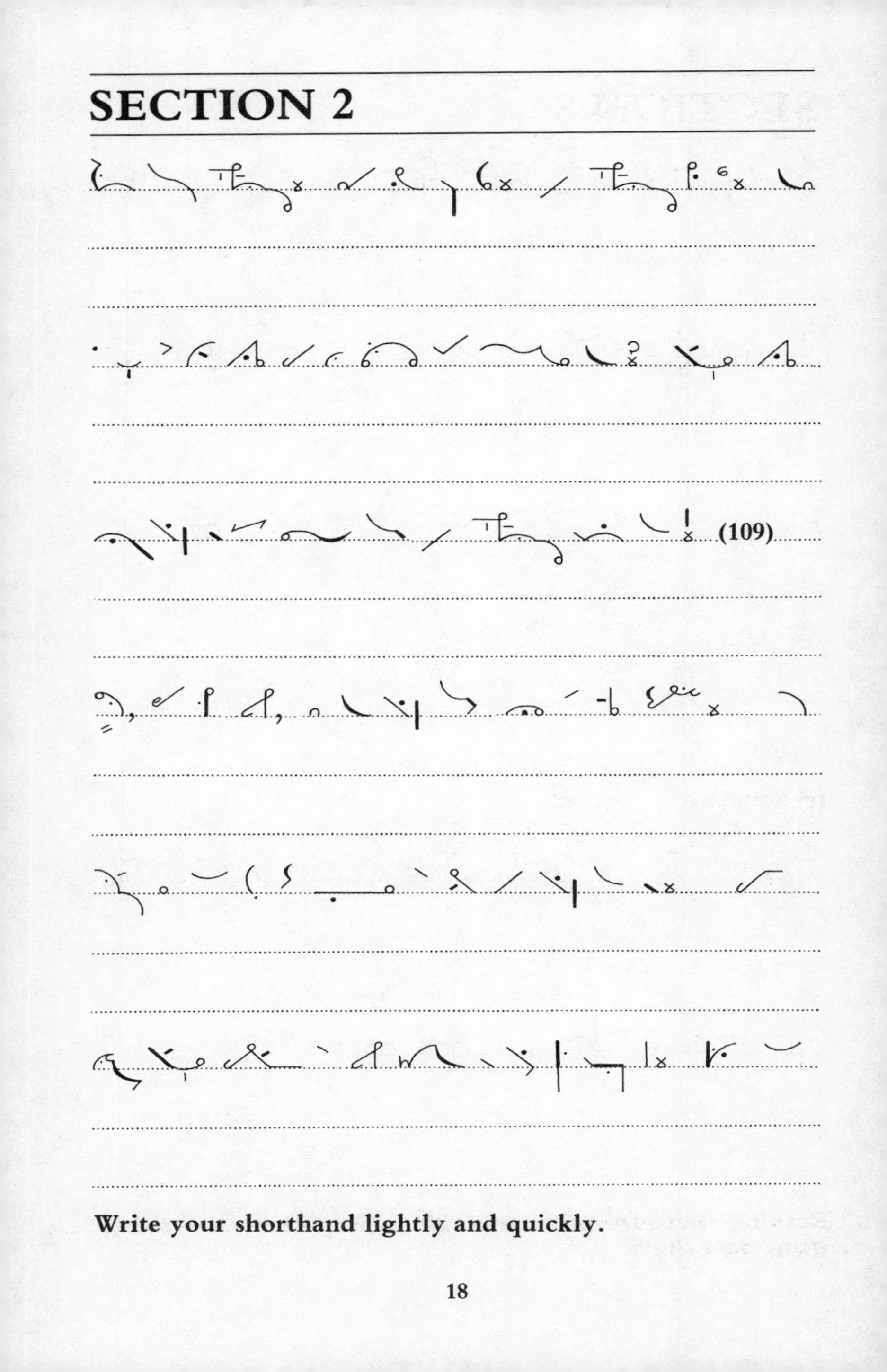

SECTION 2

(109)

Write your shorthand lightly and quickly.

SECTION 8

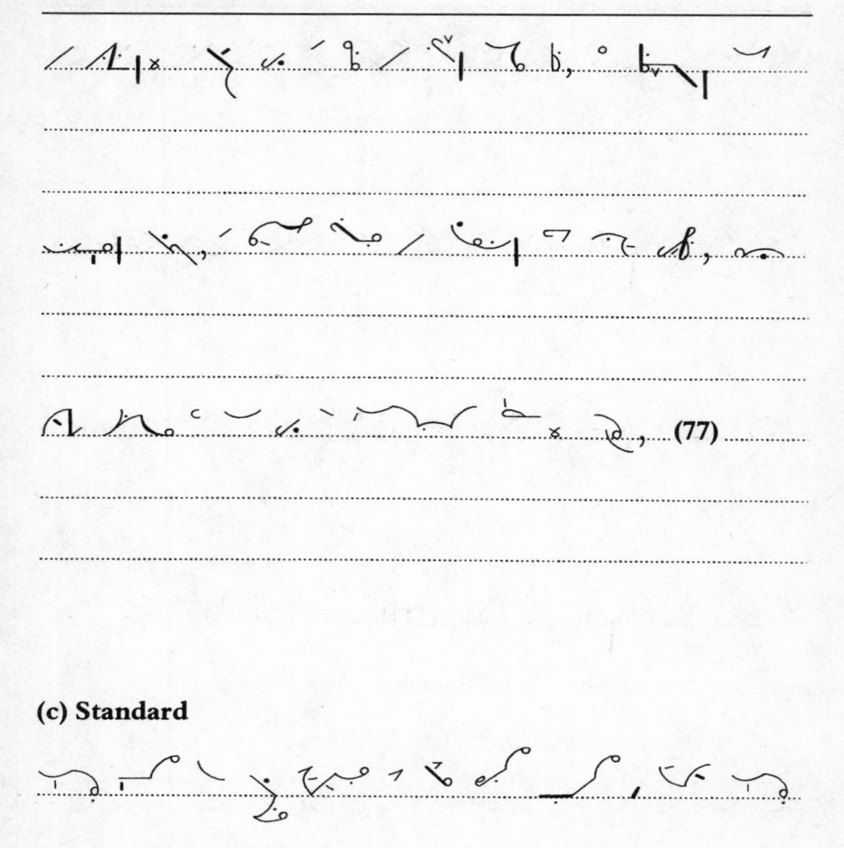

(77)

(c) Standard

Reading short forms instantly is as important as writing them instantly.

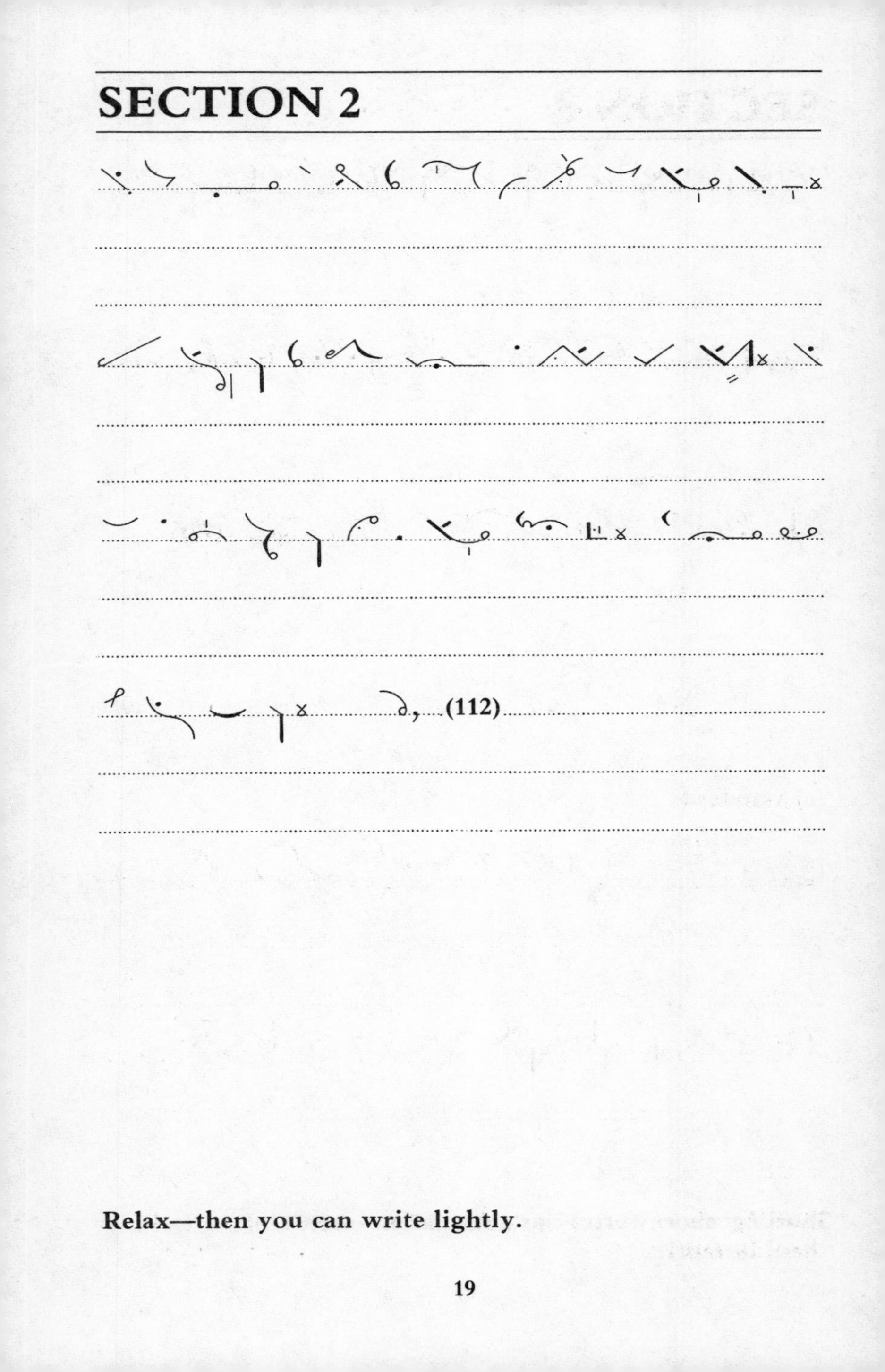

SECTION 2

(112)

Relax—then you can write lightly.

SECTION 8

(90)

Short forms have to be as automatic as ABC.

SECTION 3

Unit 7 of *Pitman 2000 First Course*

1 SHORT FORM PRACTICE

(a)

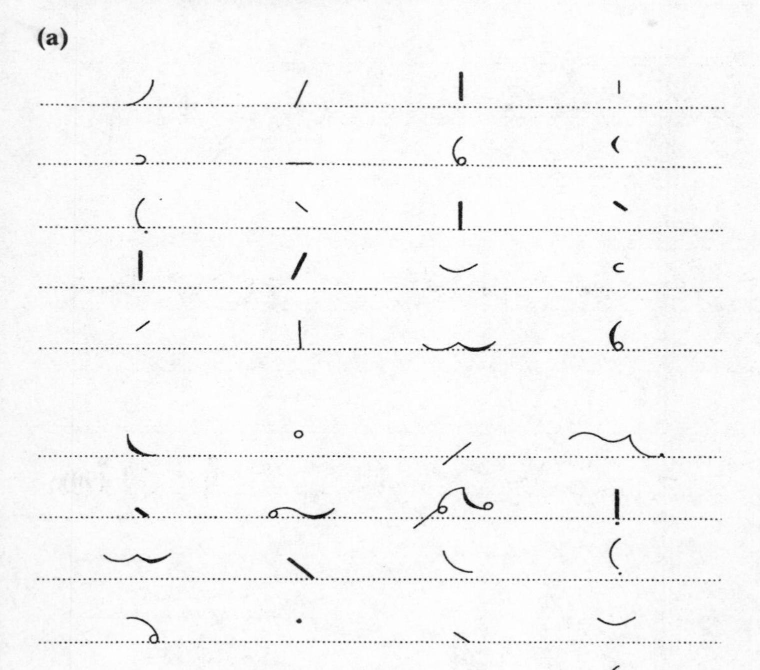

(b)

i (10)

ii (10)

iii (21)

Fill your pens with ink before each shorthand lesson.

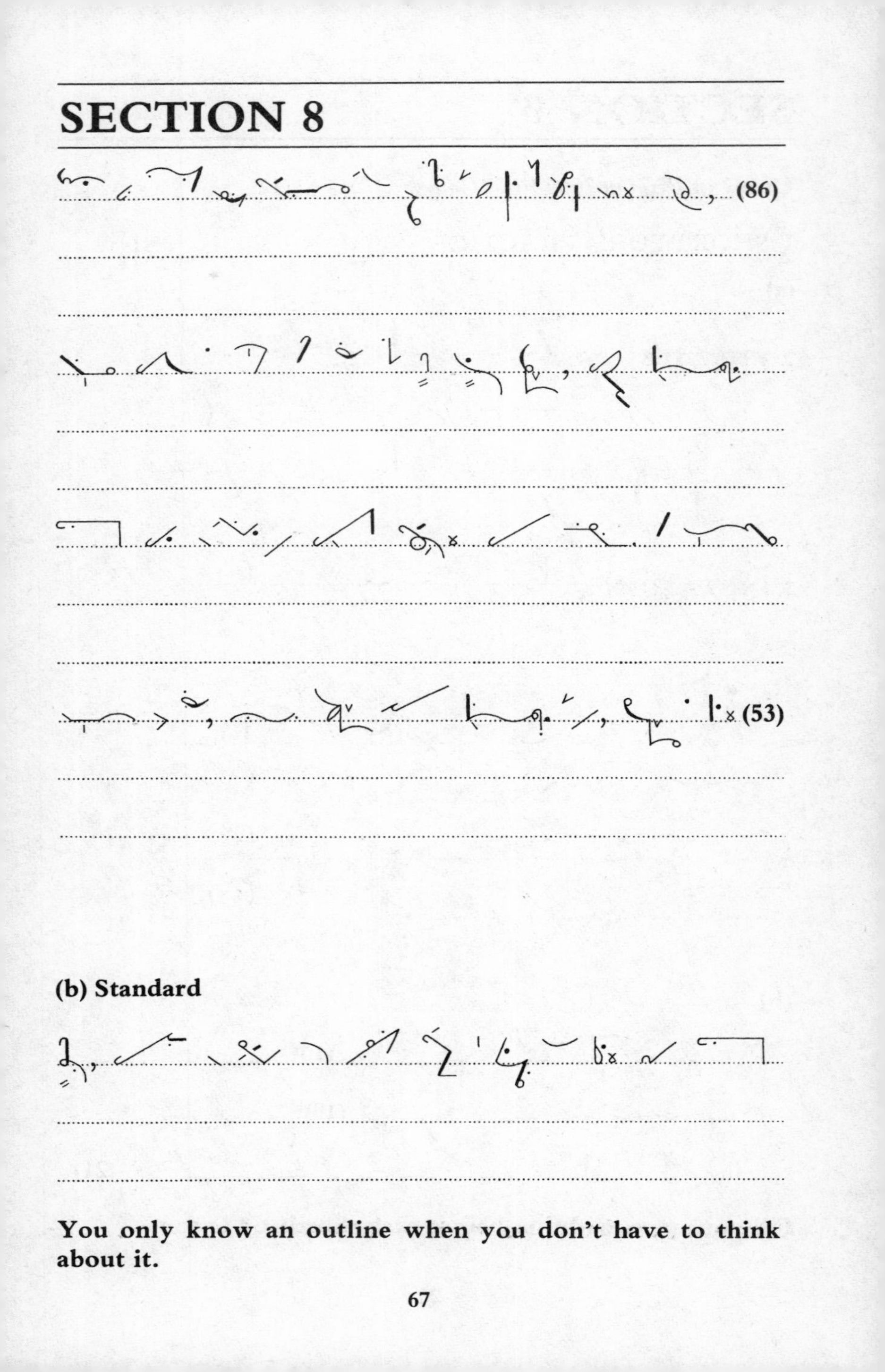

SECTION 8

(86)

(53)

(b) Standard

You only know an outline when you don't have to think about it.

SECTION 3

iv 3 (12)

v (17)

2 PHRASES

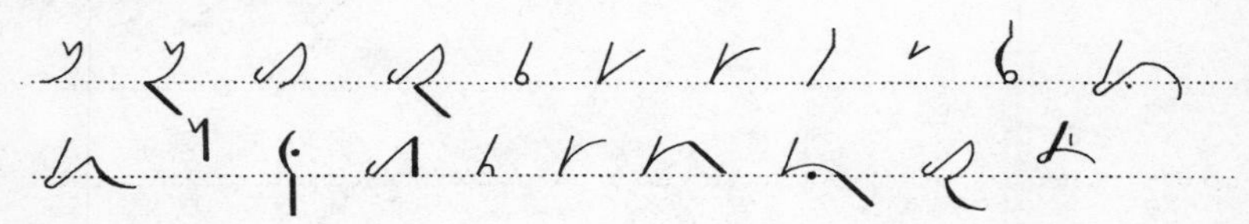

3 DICTATION

(a) Easy

(45)

Copy the shorthand swiftly—but accurately.

SECTION 8

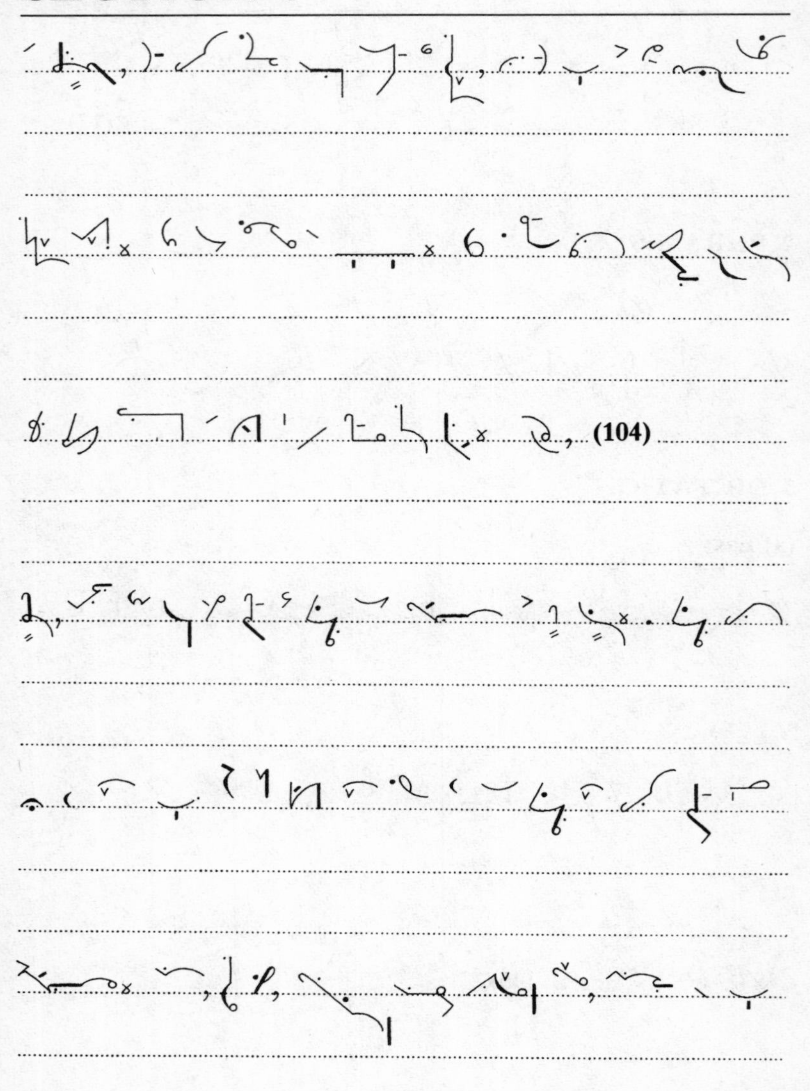

You write your name without thinking. Aim to make your shorthand equally automatic.

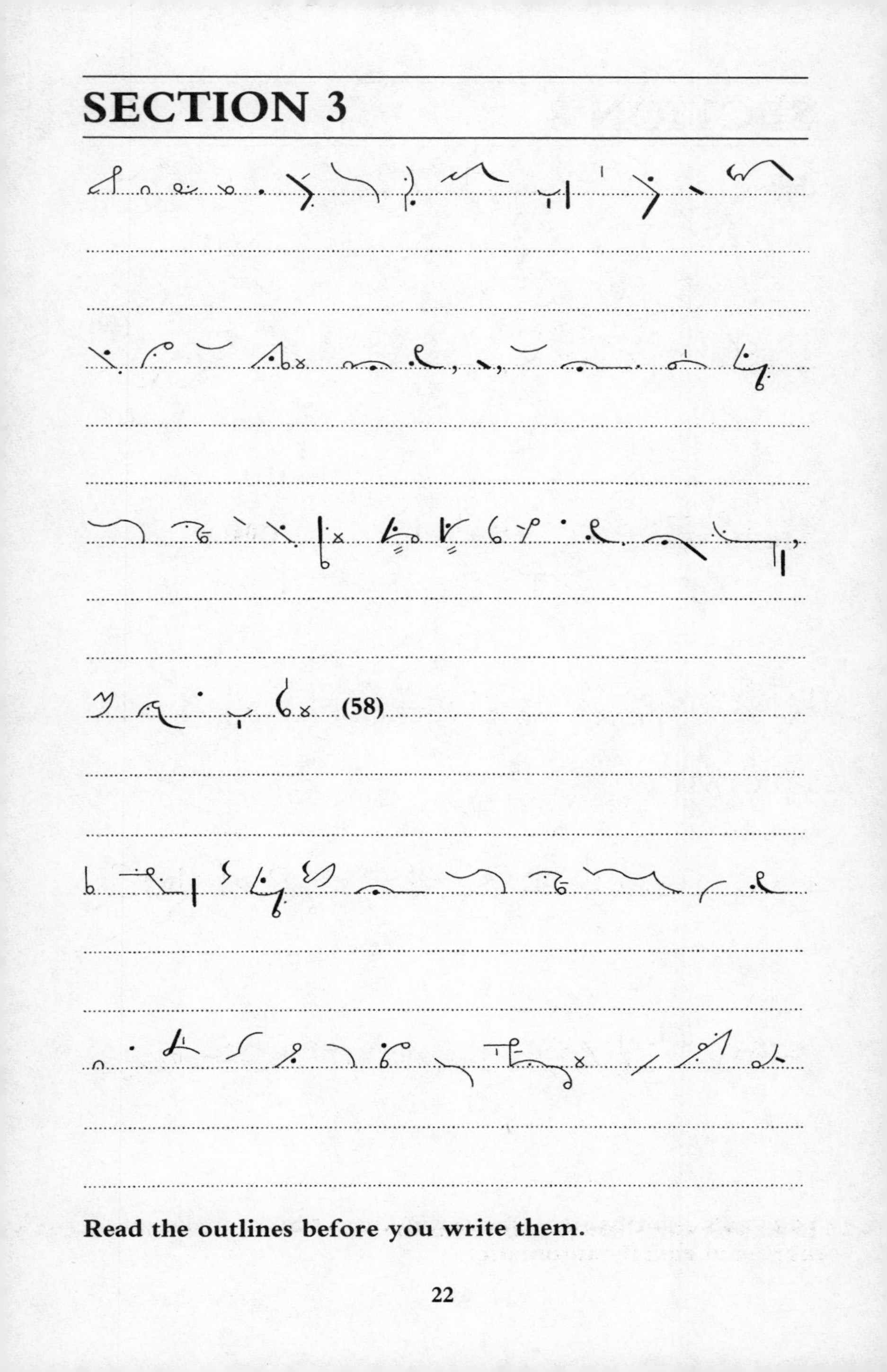

SECTION 3

(58)

Read the outlines before you write them.

SECTION 8

(b)

i .... **(14)** ....

ii .... **(19)**

iii .... **(13)** ....

iv .... **(18)**

v .... **(11)** ....

2 PHRASES

3 DICTATION

(a) Easy

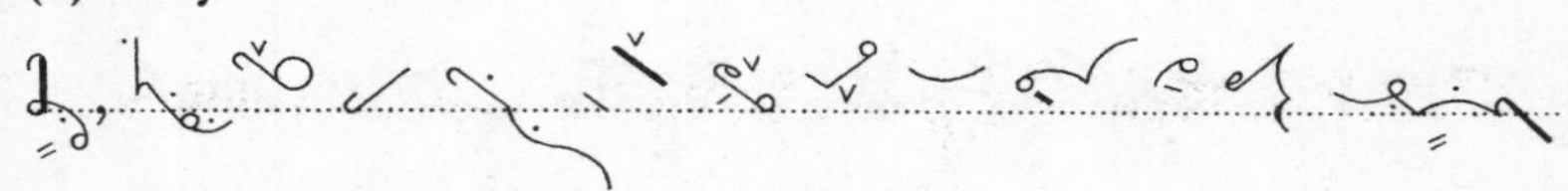

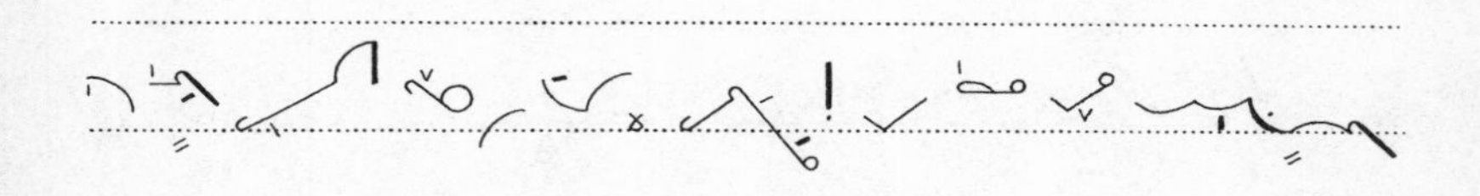

Read every outline as you write it.

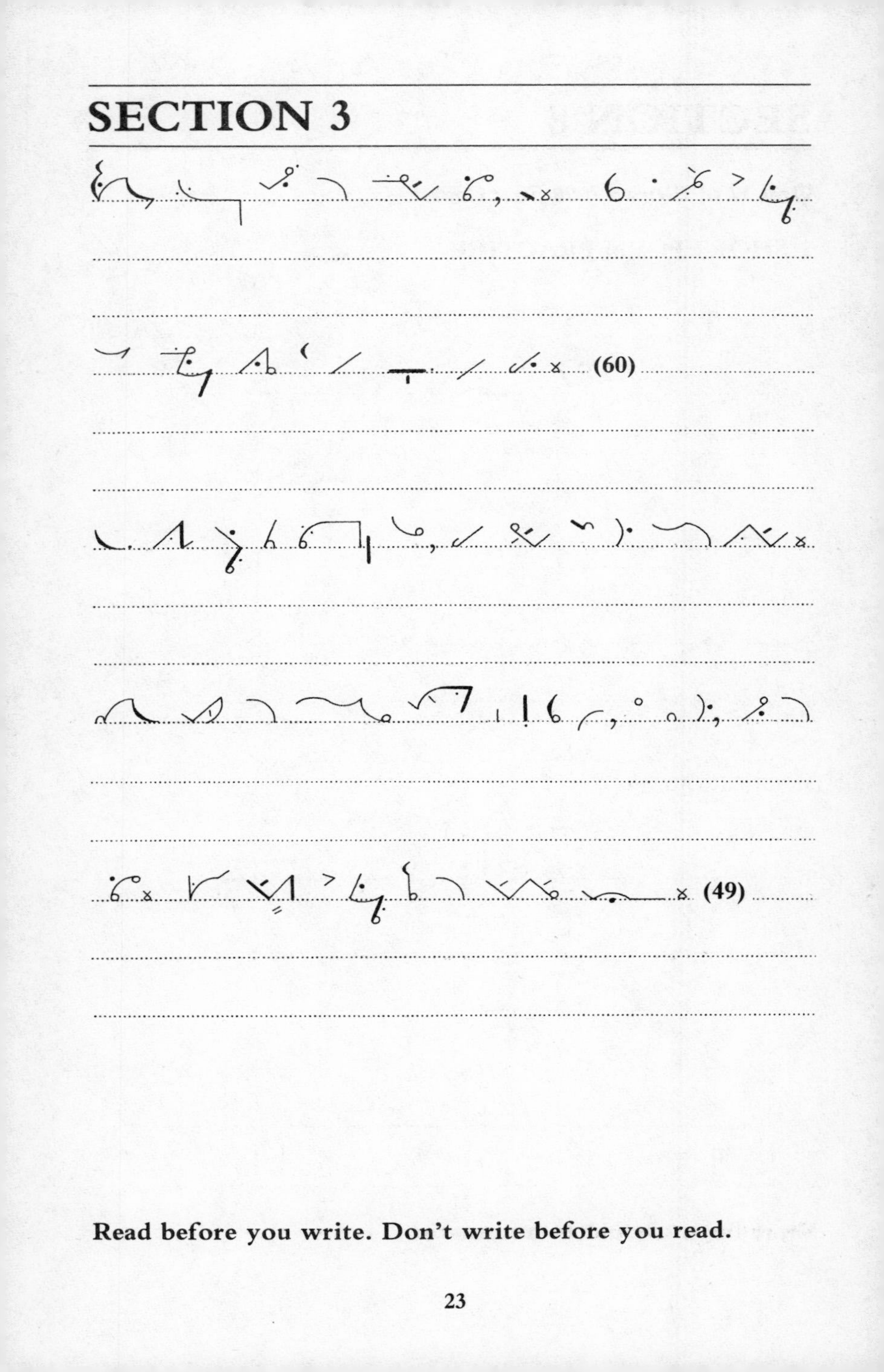

SECTION 3

(60)

(49)

Read before you write. Don't write before you read.

SECTION 8

Unit 12 of *Pitman 2000 First Course*

1 SHORT FORM PRACTICE

(a)

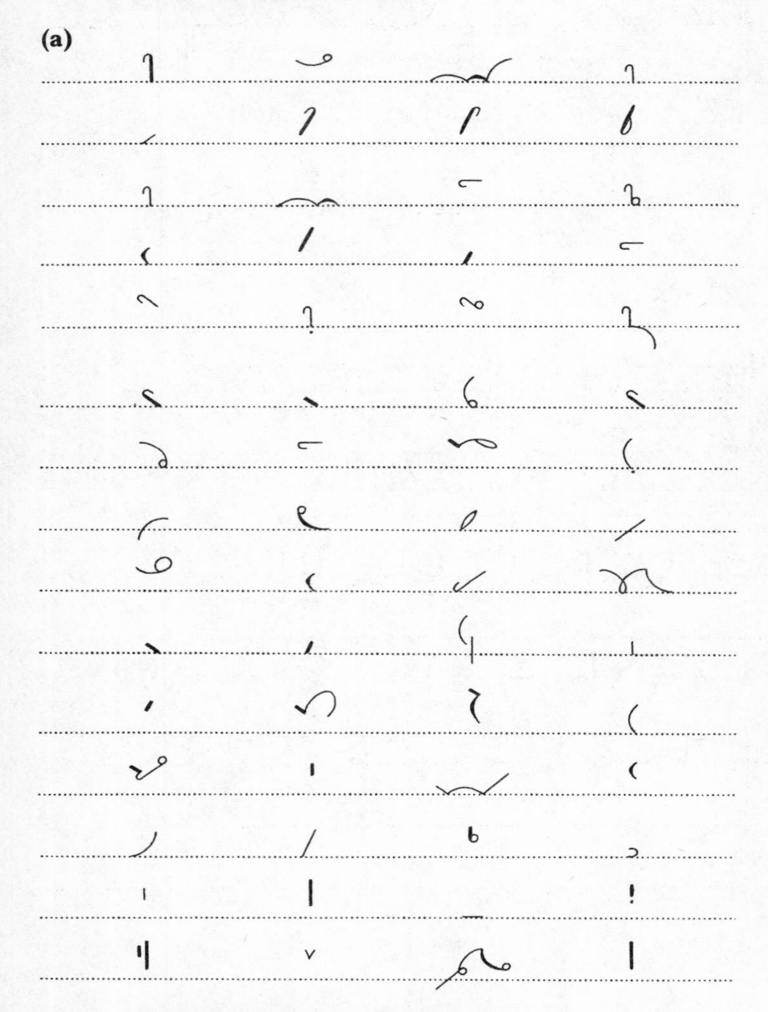

Short forms should be automatic.

SECTION 3

(b) Standard

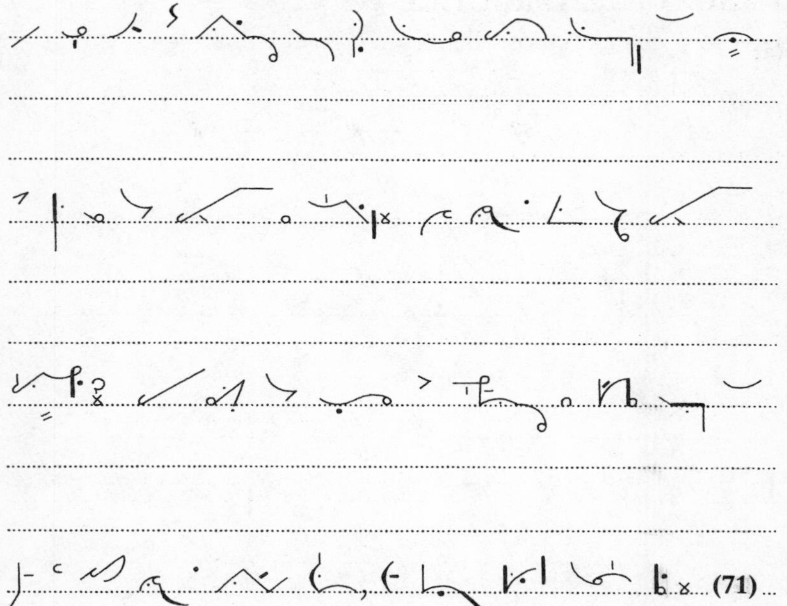

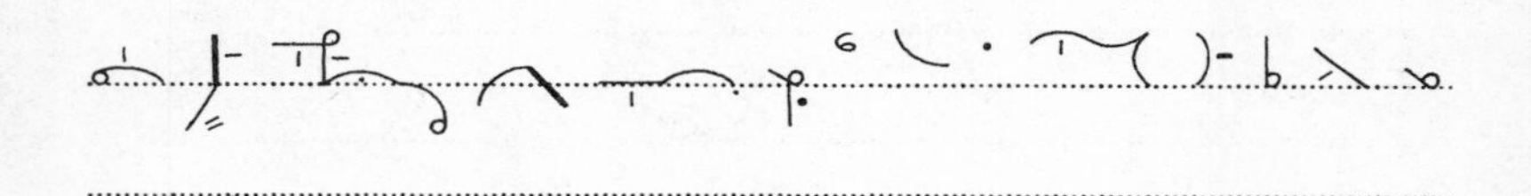

Do not write what you do not read.

SECTION 7

(93)

You should aim to read 70 words in every 30 seconds.

SECTION 3

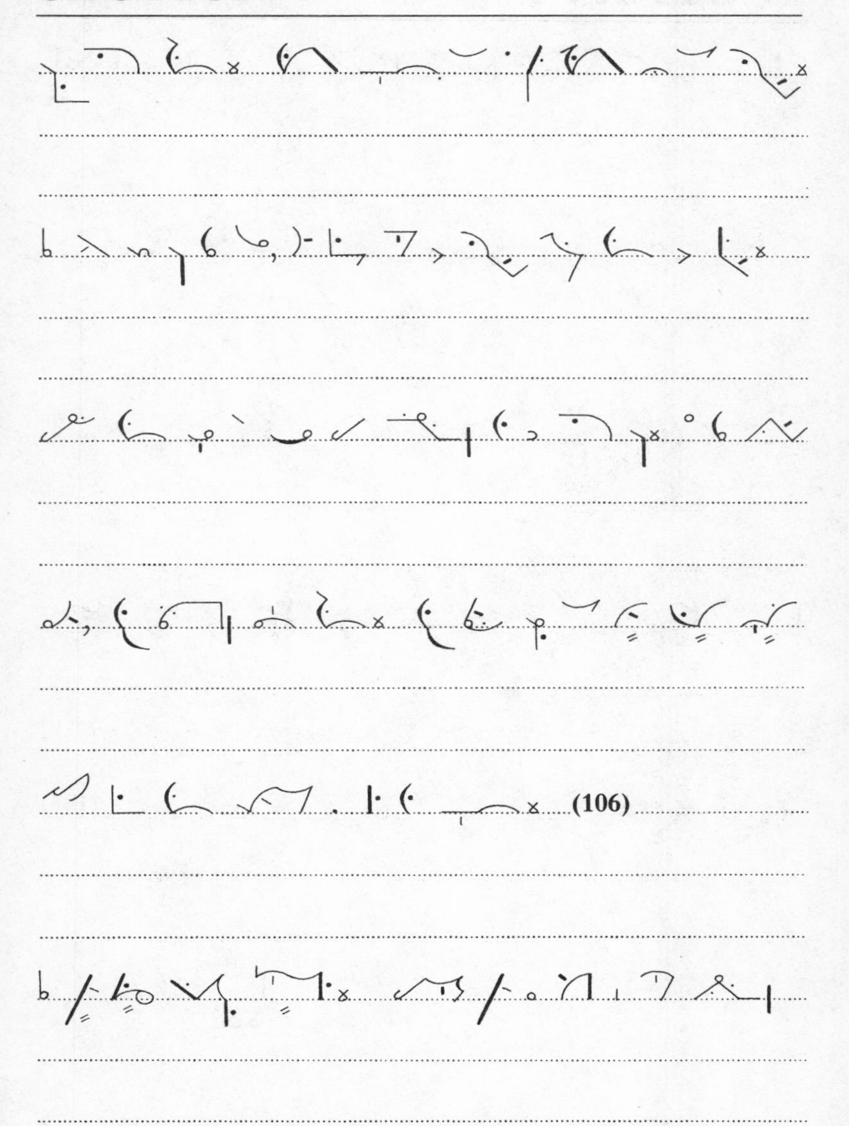

Good shorthand writing is only half the battle—good shorthand reading is the other half.

SECTION 7

(104)

Practise your 'reading aloud' speed on the shorthand in this workbook.

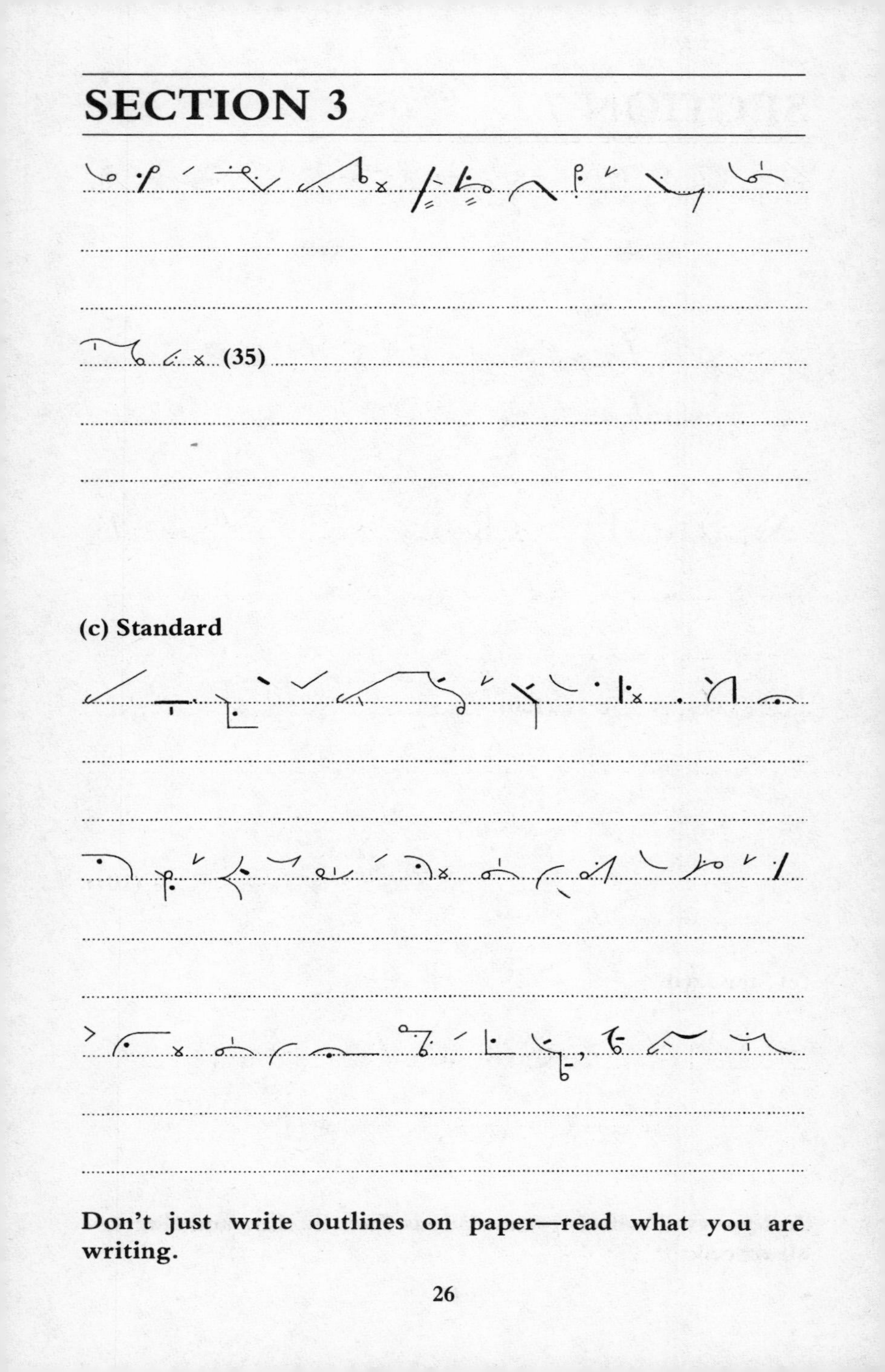

SECTION 3

(35)

(c) Standard

Don't just write outlines on paper—read what you are writing.

SECTION 7

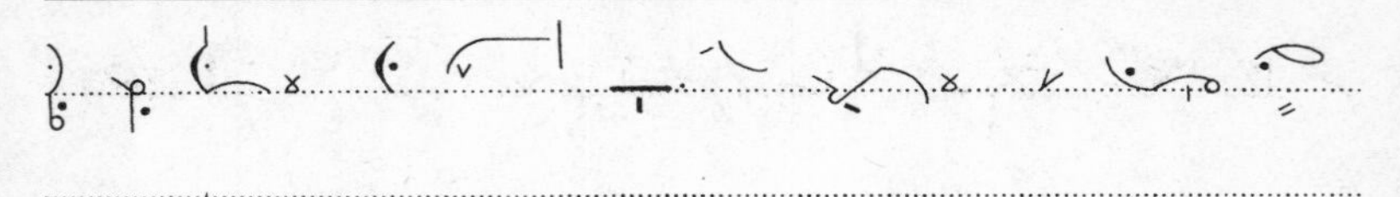

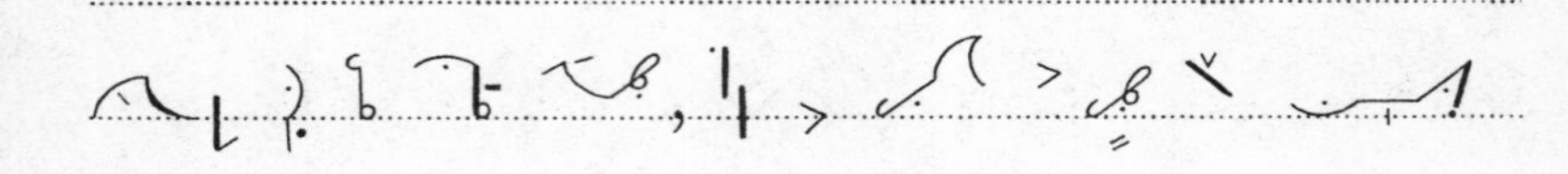

(150)

(c) Standard

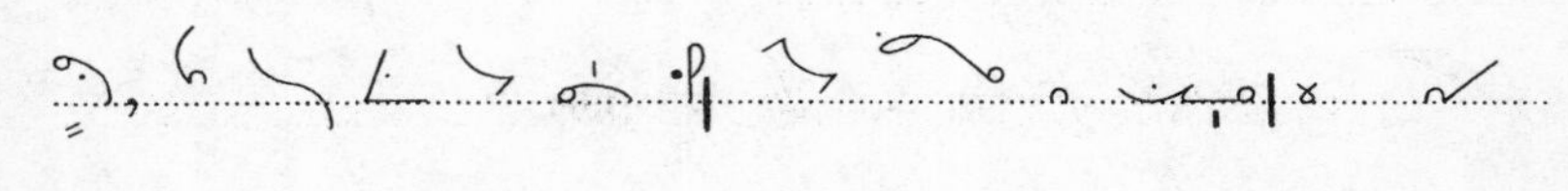

Ask yourself whether your pen is fine, flexible and fluent—all three.

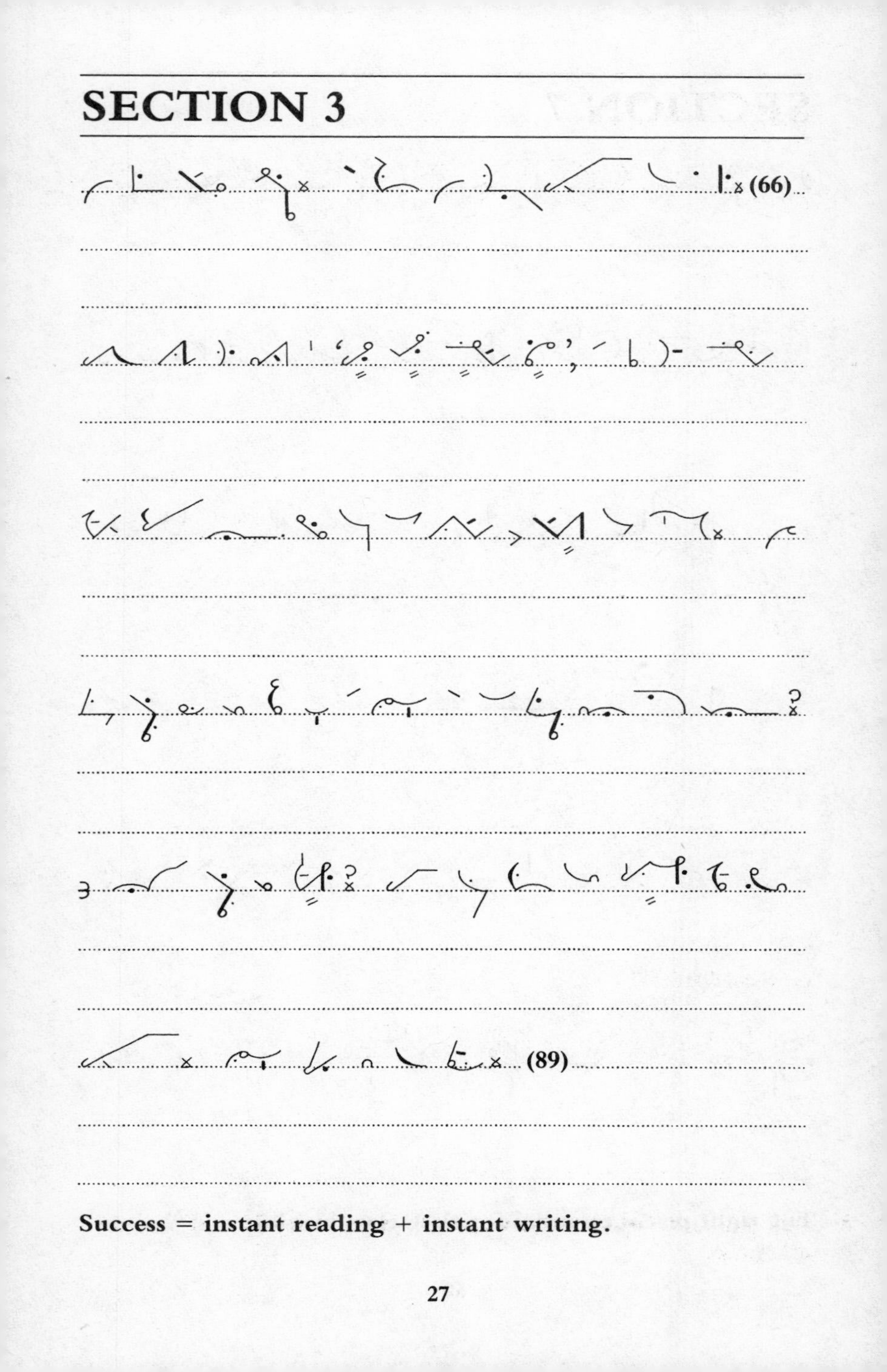

SECTION 3

(66)

(89)

Success = instant reading + instant writing.

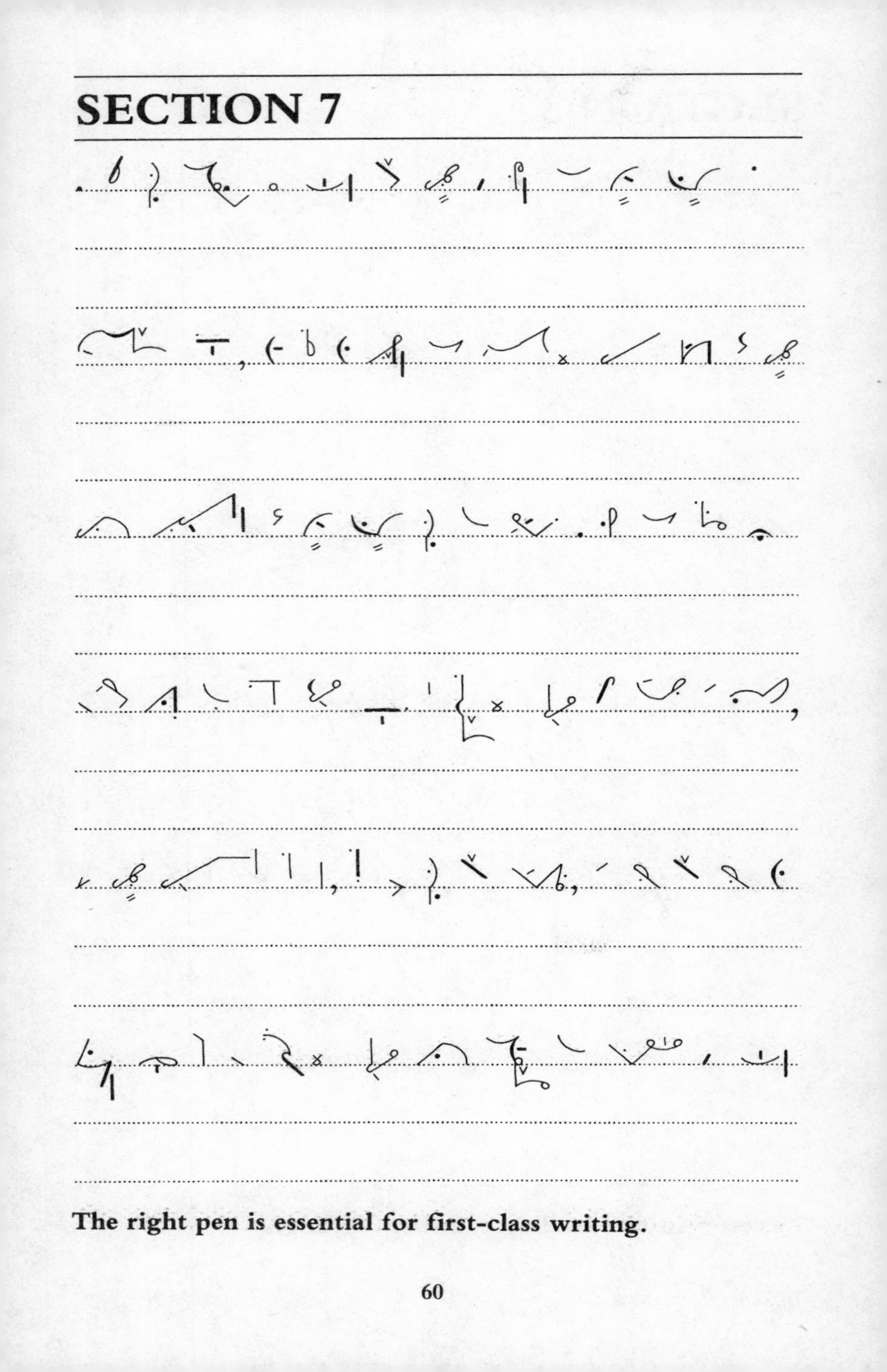

SECTION 7

The right pen is essential for first-class writing.

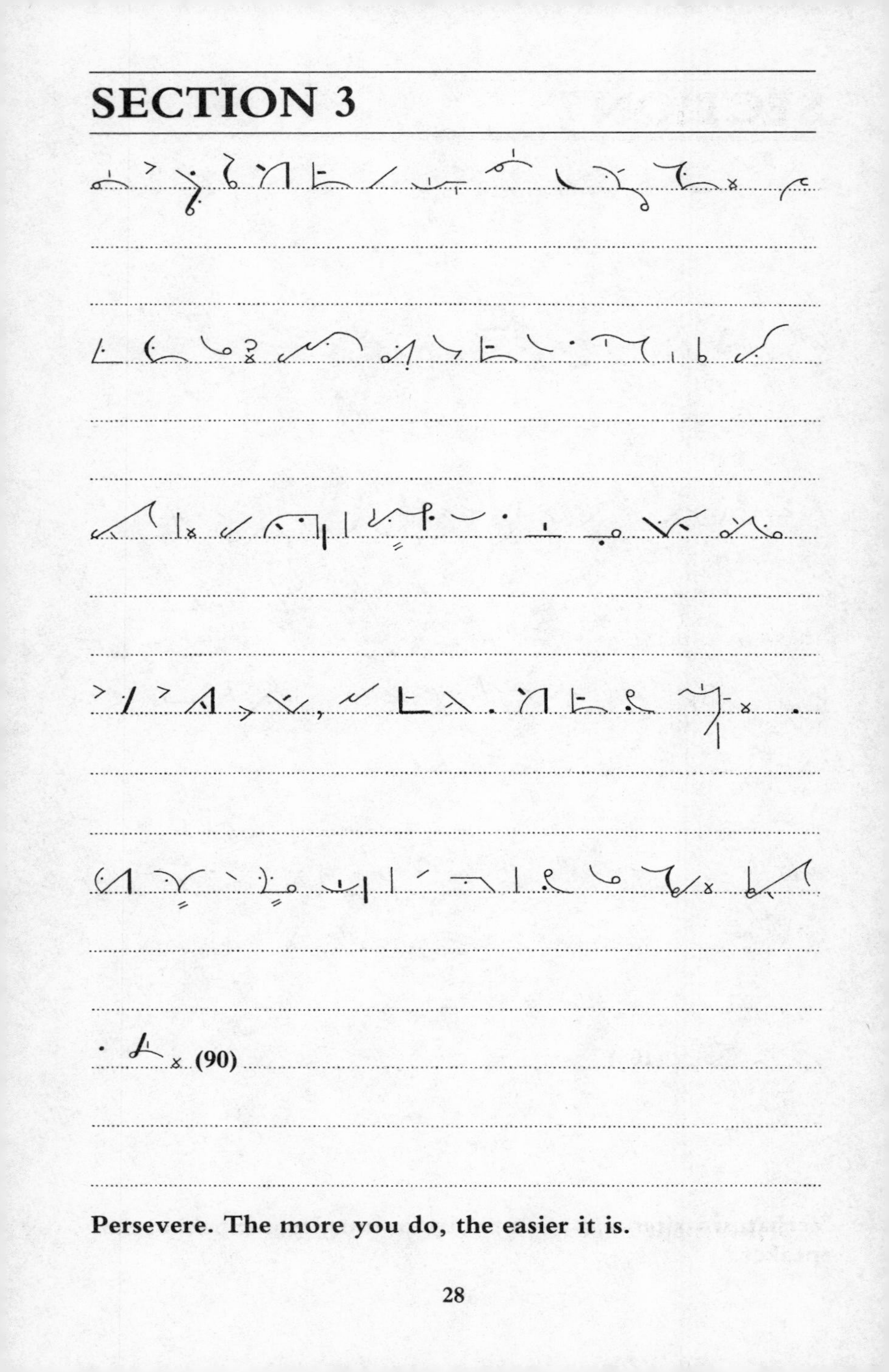

SECTION 3

(90)

Persevere. The more you do, the easier it is.

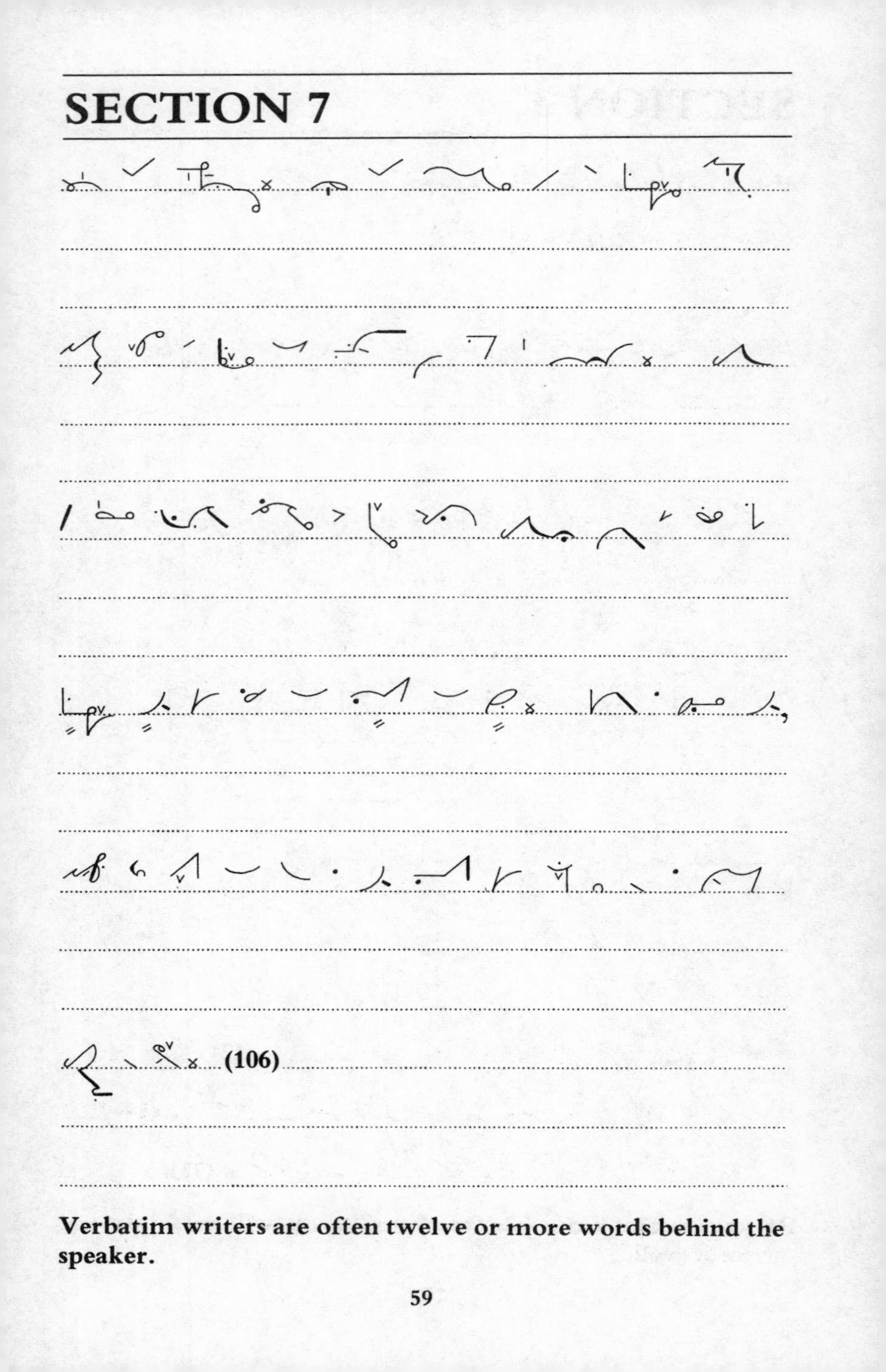

SECTION 7

(106)

Verbatim writers are often twelve or more words behind the speaker.

SECTION 4

Unit 8 of *Pitman 2000 First Course*

1 SHORT FORM PRACTICE

(a)

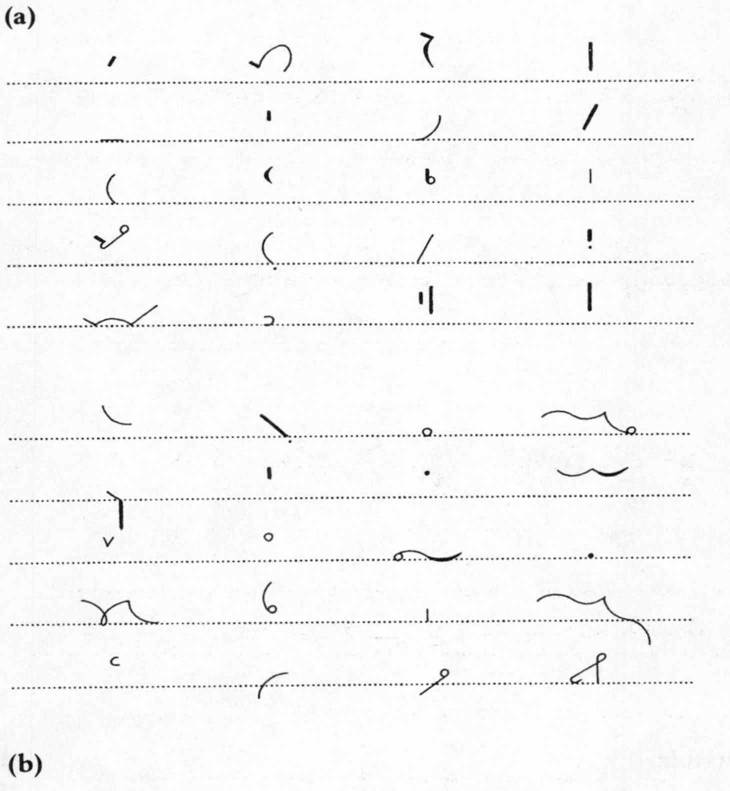

(b)

i .... (12) ....

ii .... (14) ....

iii .... (11) ....

If you cannot read shorthand well, you will certainly not write it well.

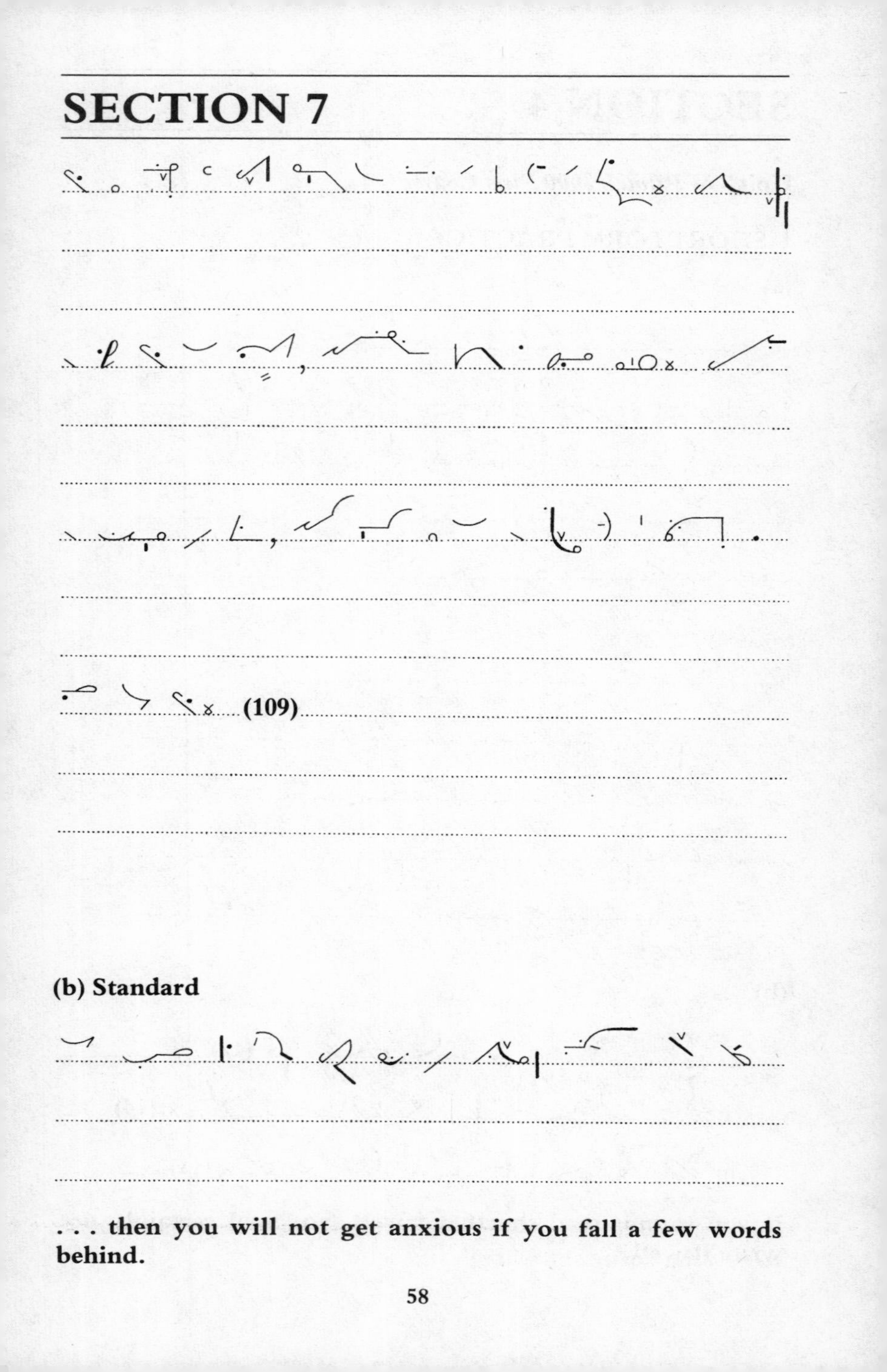

SECTION 7

(109)

(b) Standard

. . . then you will not get anxious if you fall a few words behind.

SECTION 4

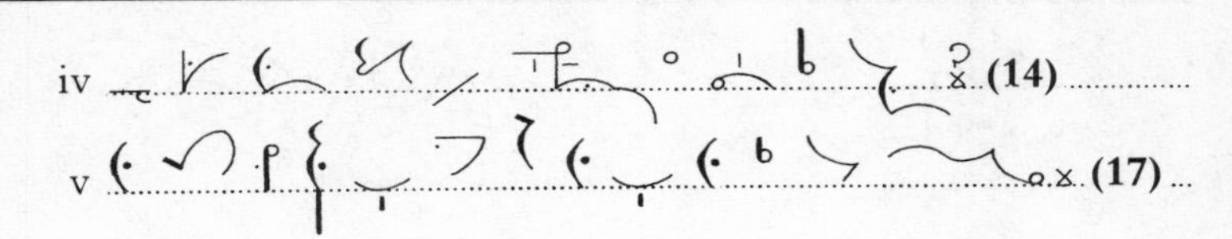

2 PHRASES

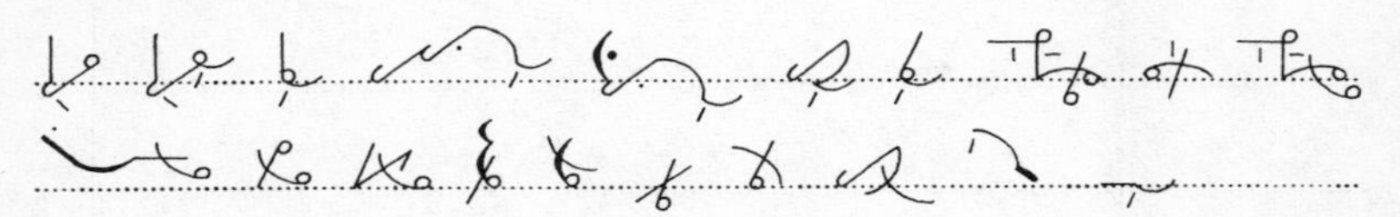

3 DICTATION

(a) Easy

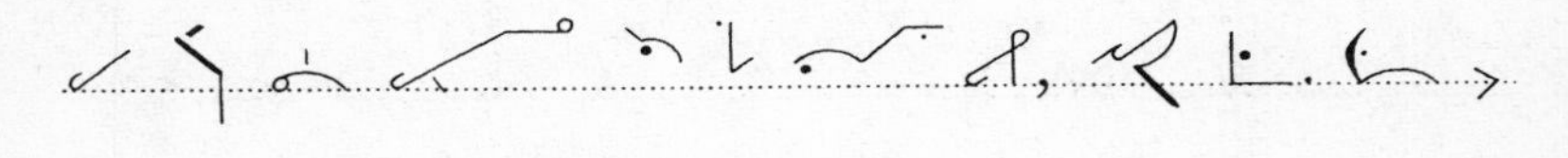

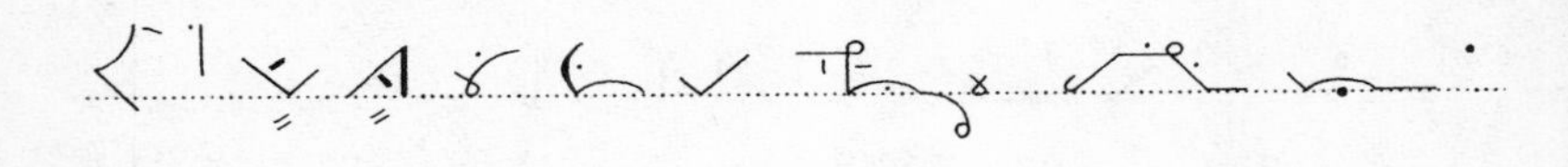

Spend 15 minutes of your own time daily in reading and re-reading some shorthand.

SECTION 7

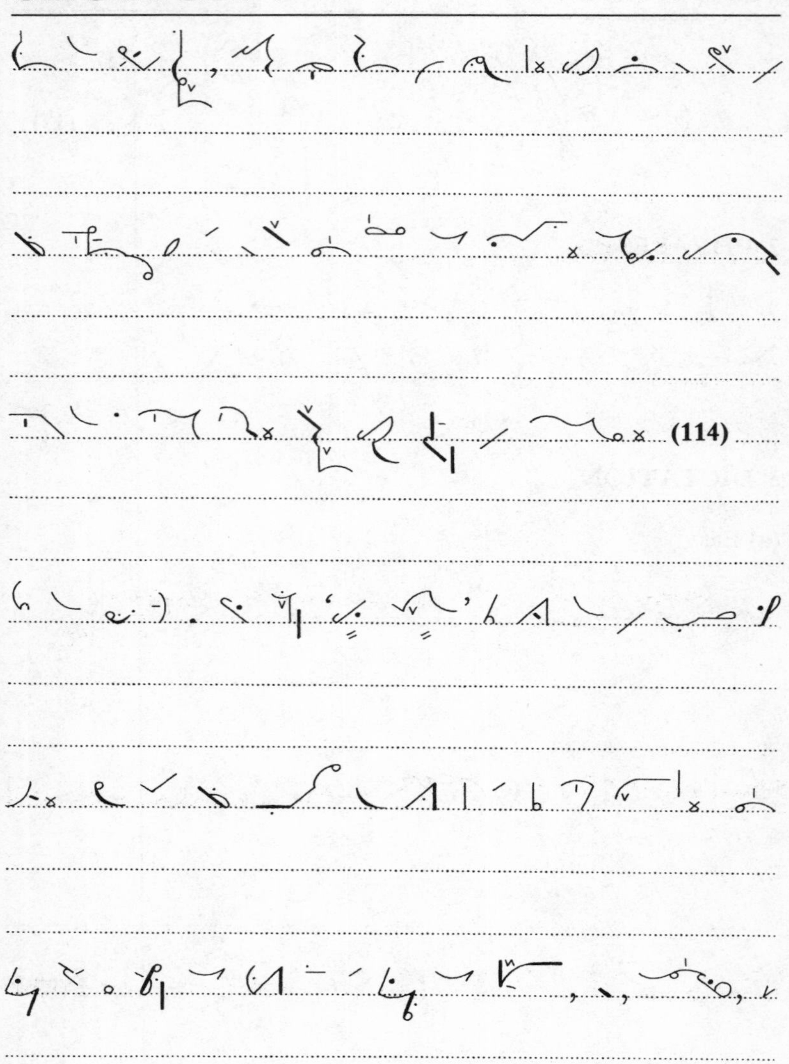

(114)

Learn to store 10–20 words mentally . . .

SECTION 4

(73)

(83)

Keep cool and relaxed during dictation.

SECTION 7

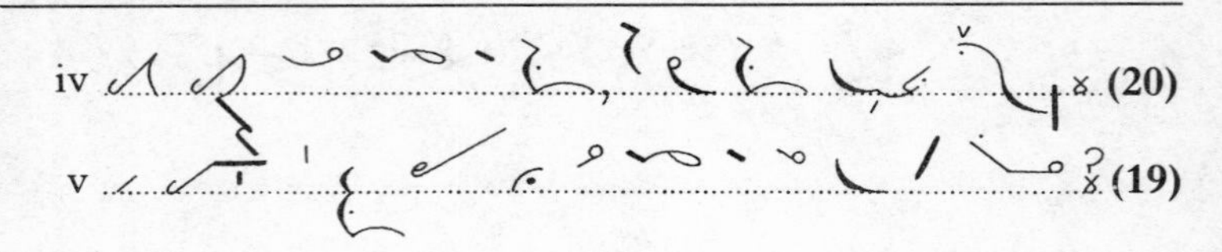

2 PHRASES

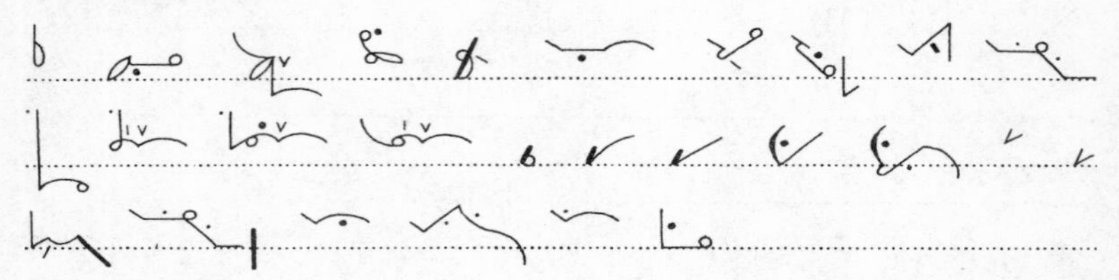

3 DICTATION

(a) Easy

'Thin' strokes are very thin; 'thick' strokes are slightly firmer.

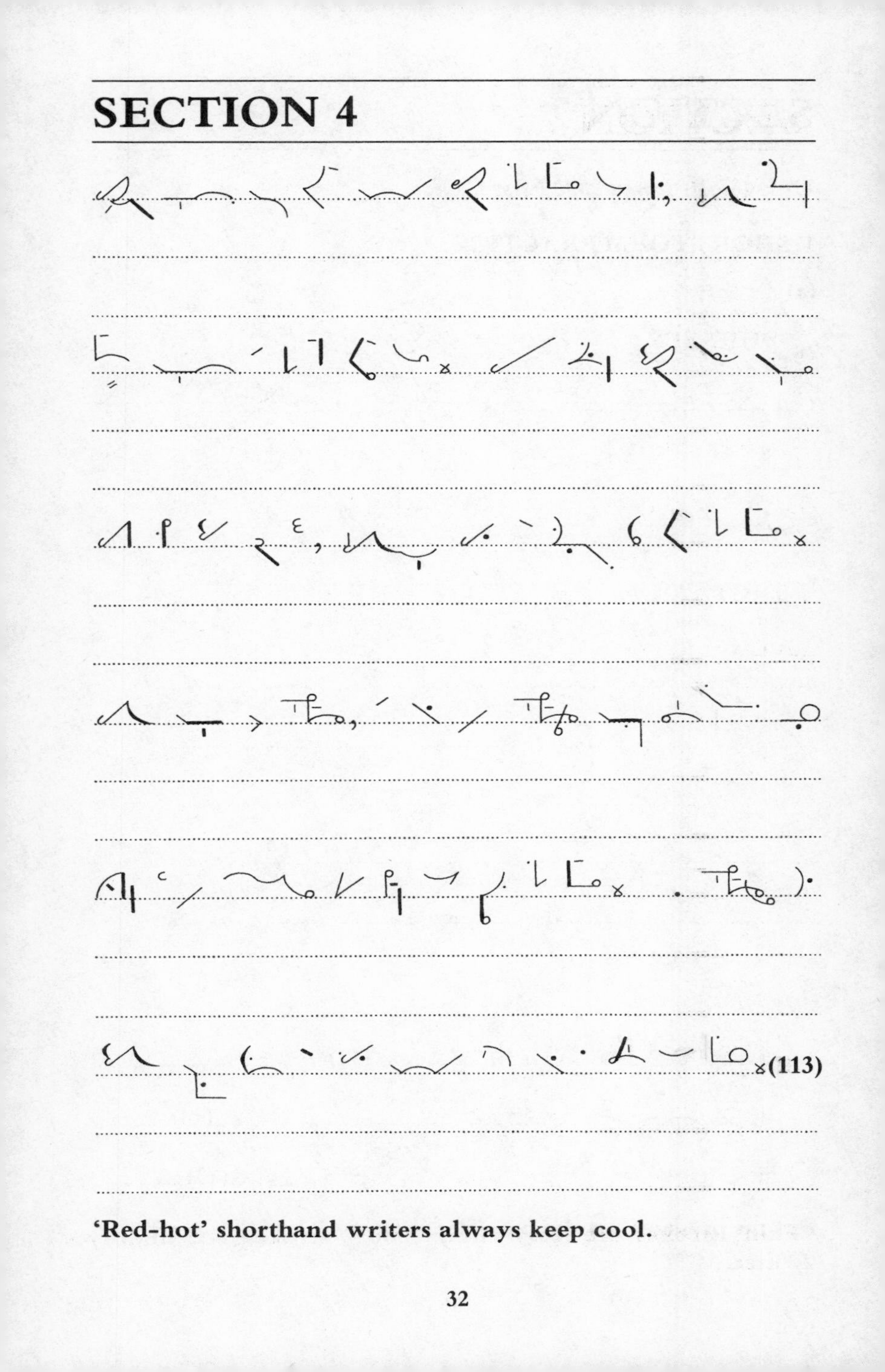

SECTION 4

(113)

'Red-hot' shorthand writers always keep cool.

SECTION 7

Unit 11 of *Pitman 2000 First Course*

1 SHORT FORM PRACTICE

(a)

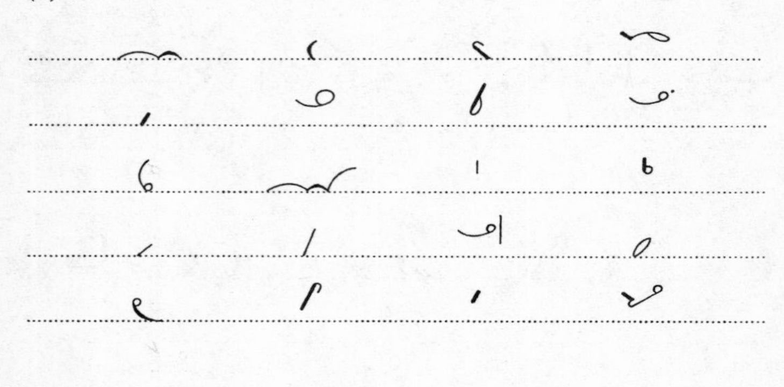

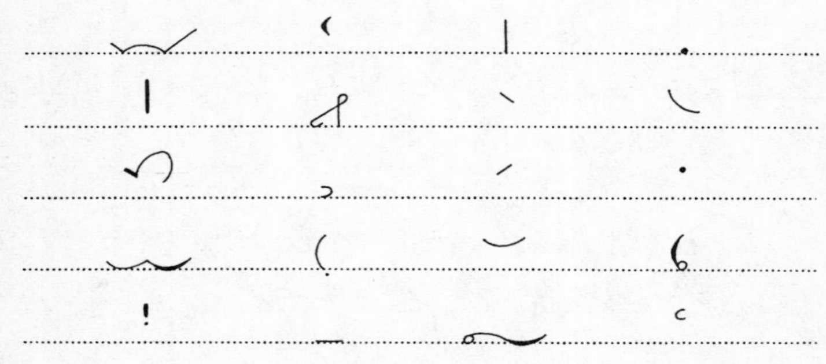

(b)

i (11)

ii (14)

iii (13)

Put no pressure on the pen—let it flow.

SECTION 4

(b) Standard

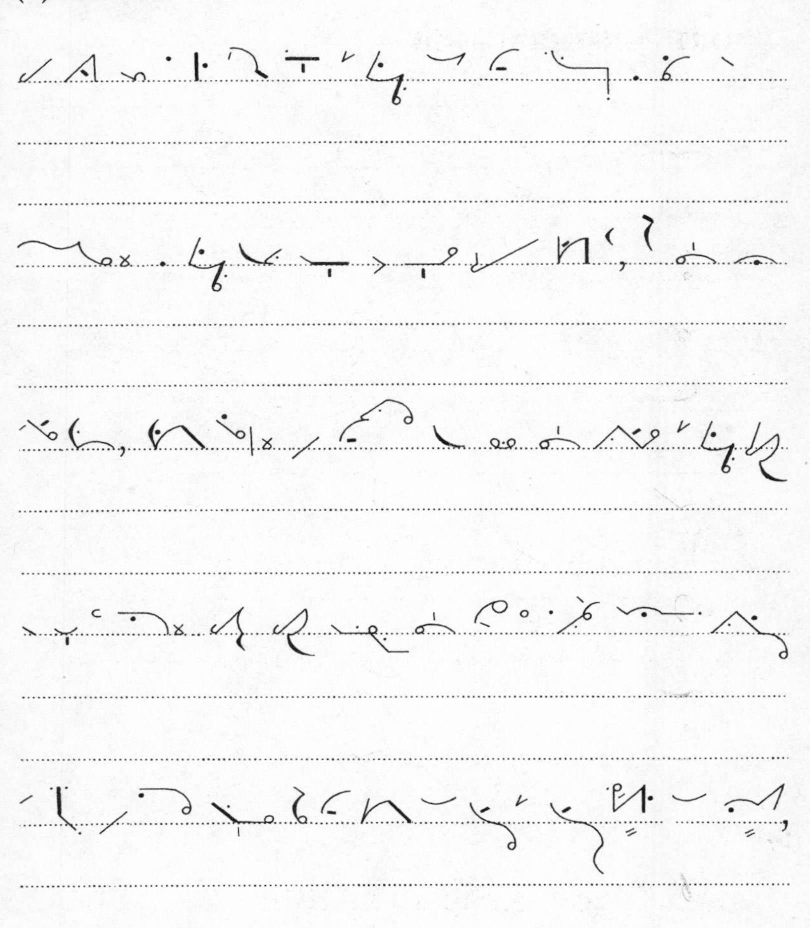

Have two pens ready in case one fails.

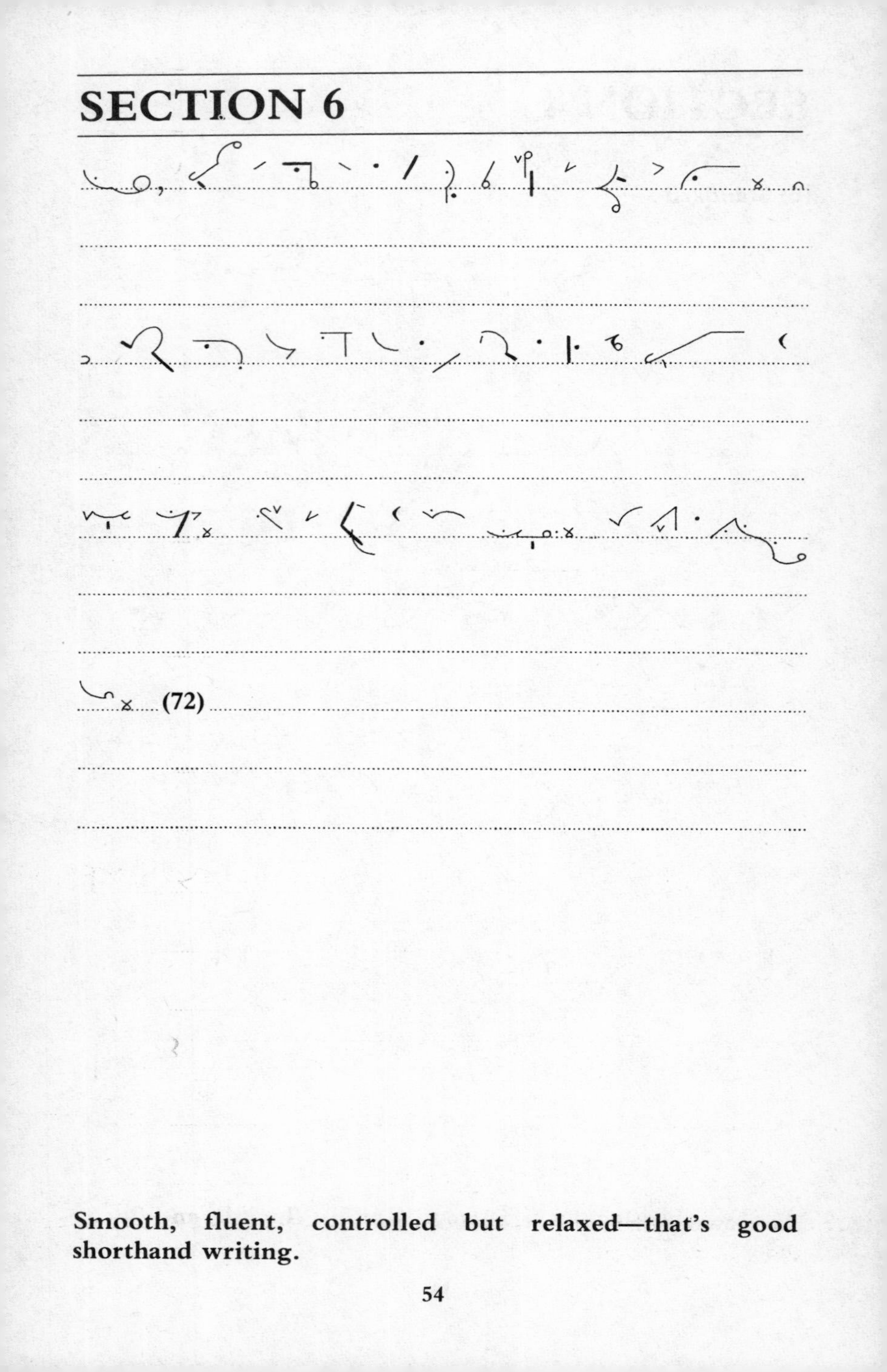

SECTION 6

(72)

Smooth, fluent, controlled but relaxed—that's good shorthand writing.

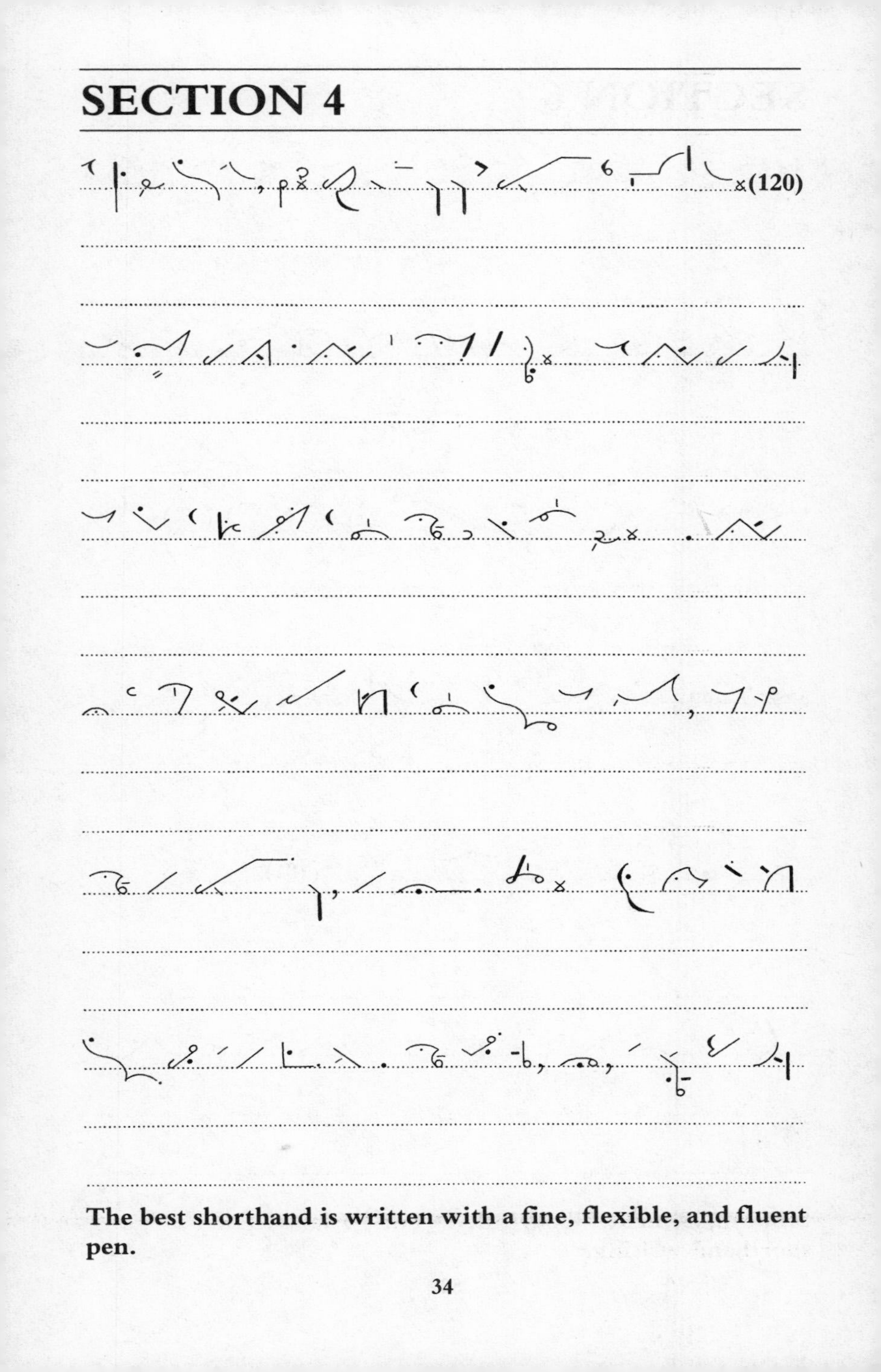

SECTION 4

(120)

The best shorthand is written with a fine, flexible, and fluent pen.

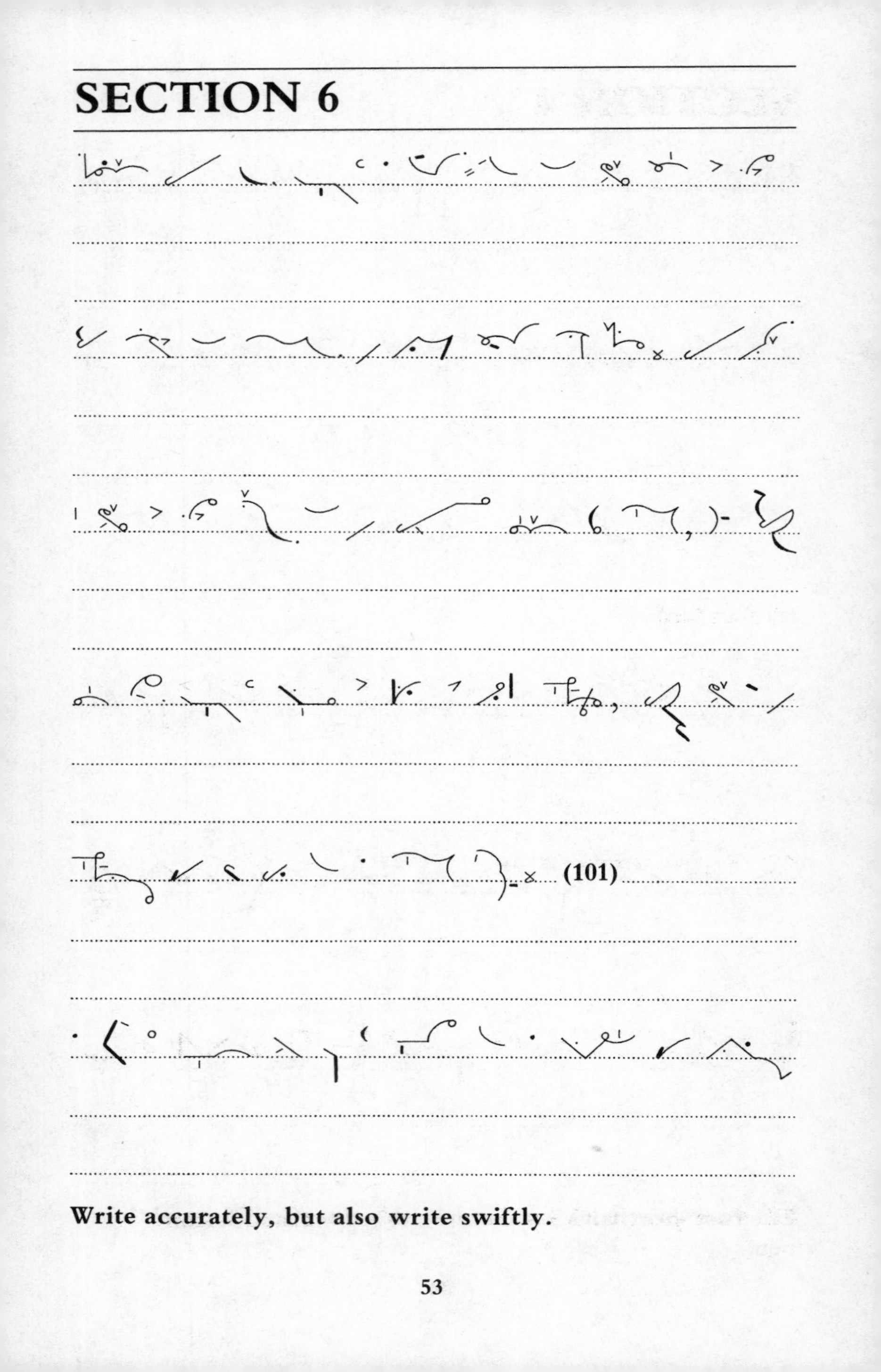

SECTION 6

(101)

Write accurately, but also write swiftly.

SECTION 4

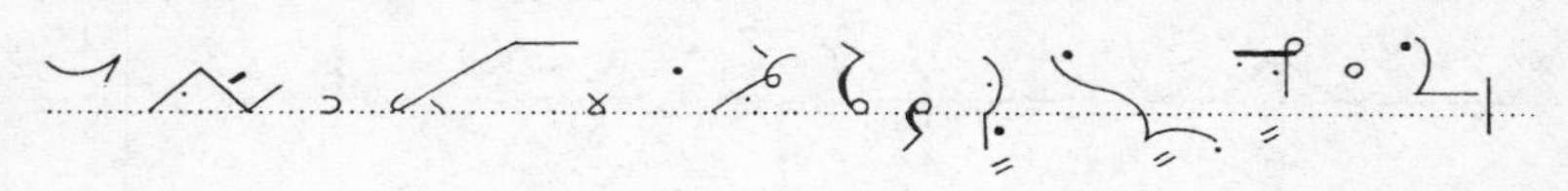

(112)

(c) Standard

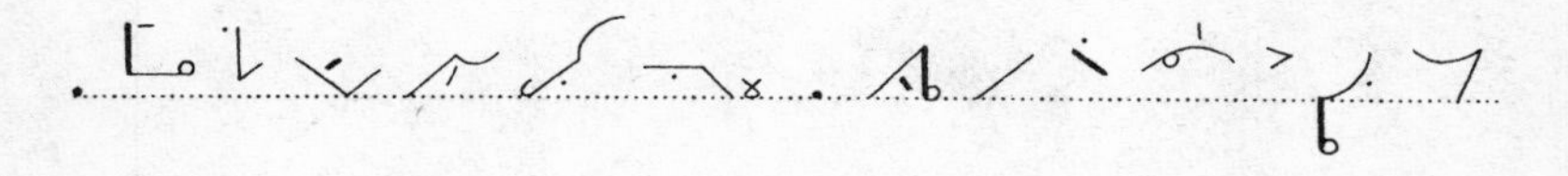

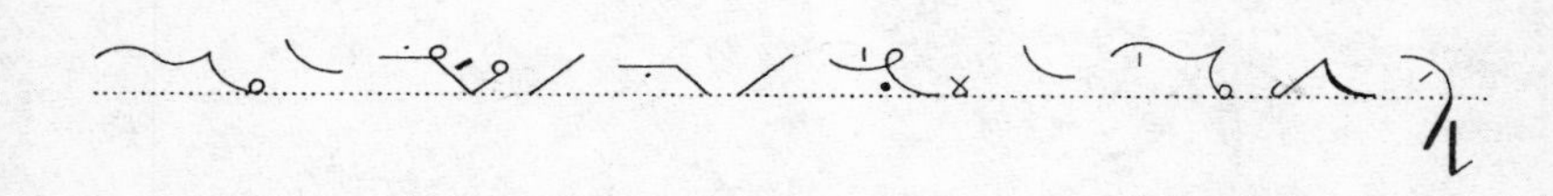

Fill your pens with ink before each shorthand lesson.

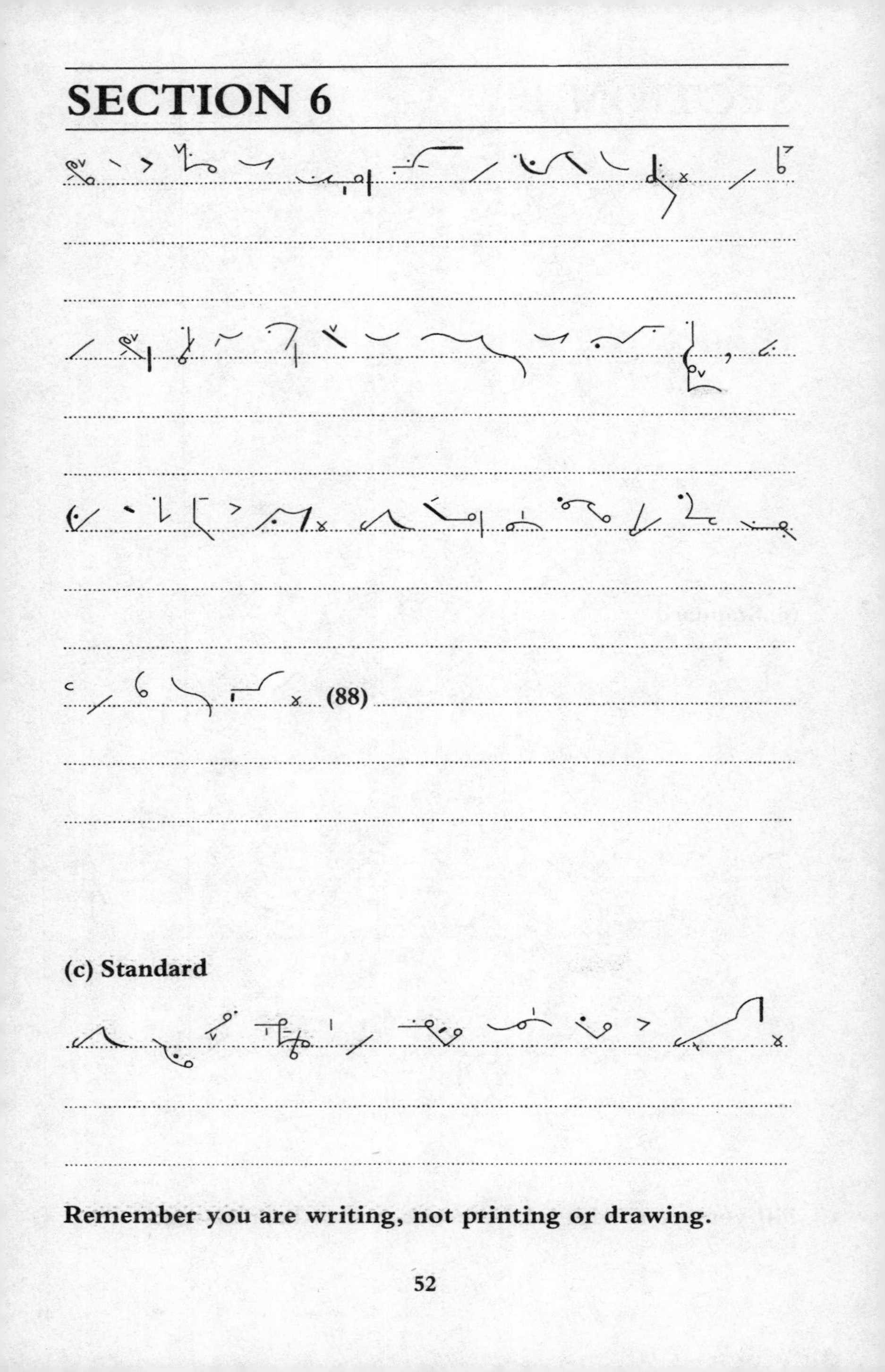

SECTION 6

(88)

(c) Standard

Remember you are writing, not printing or drawing.

SECTION 4

(112)

You need a flexible nib in your pen so that you can distinguish thick from thin.

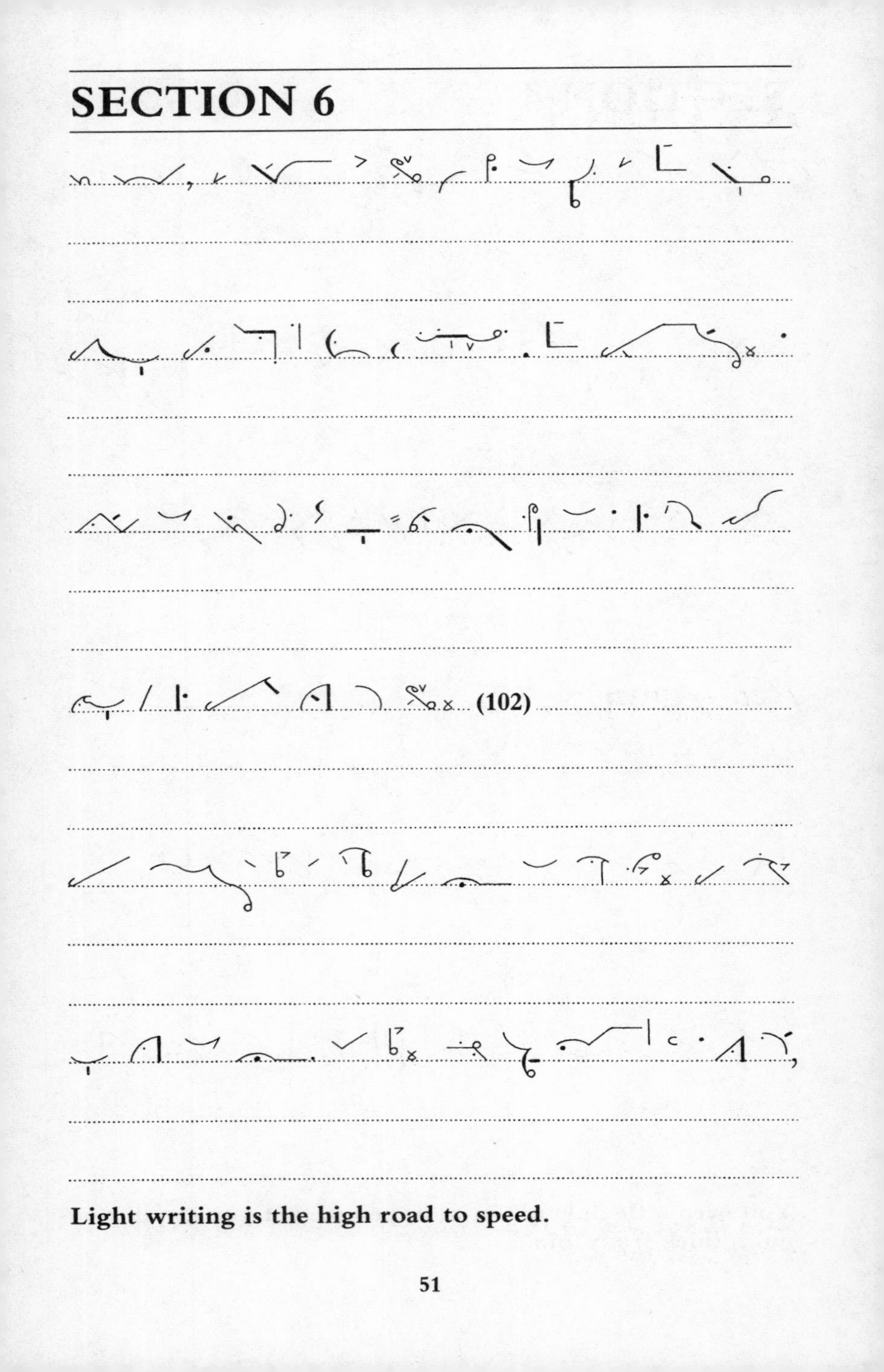

SECTION 6

(102)

Light writing is the high road to speed.

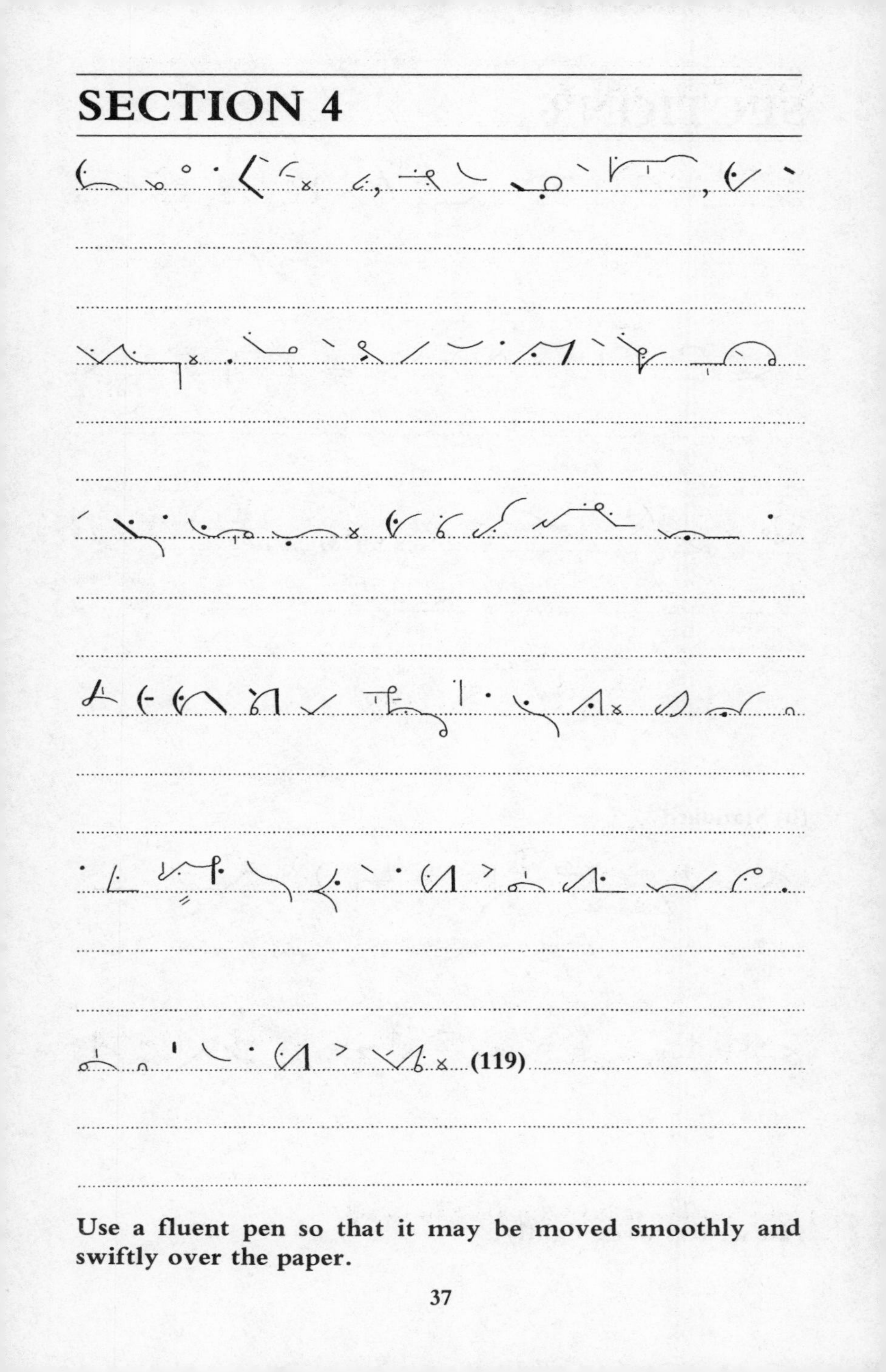

SECTION 4

(119)

Use a fluent pen so that it may be moved smoothly and swiftly over the paper.

SECTION 6

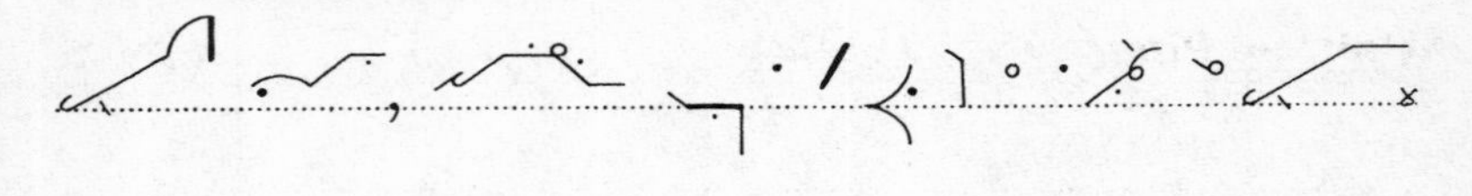

(75)

(b) Standard

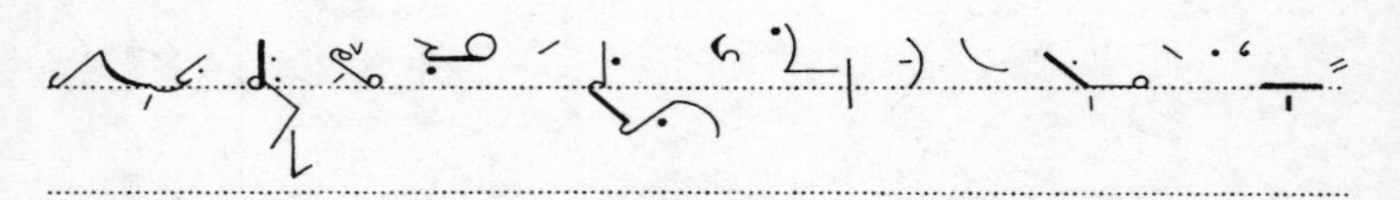

Fast writers write lightly.

SECTION 5

Unit 9 of *Pitman 2000 First Course*

1 SHORT FORM PRACTICE

(a)

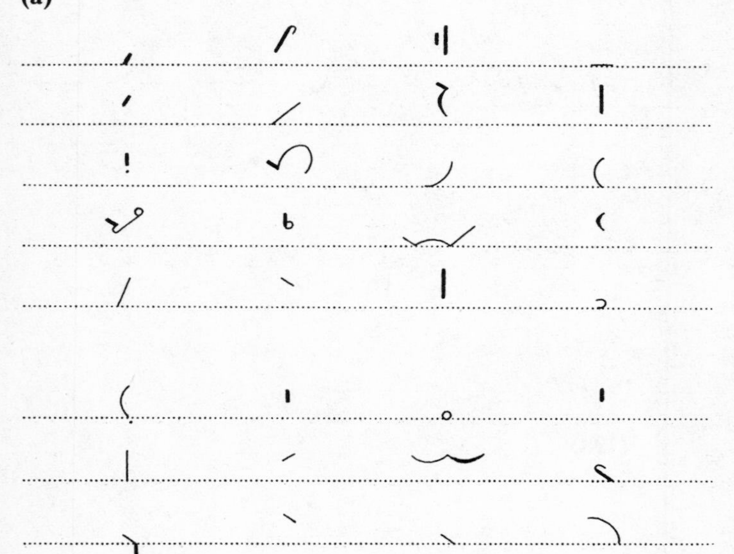

(b)

i (13)

ii (15)

iii (14)

One of the most important things to remember when writing is to write lightly.

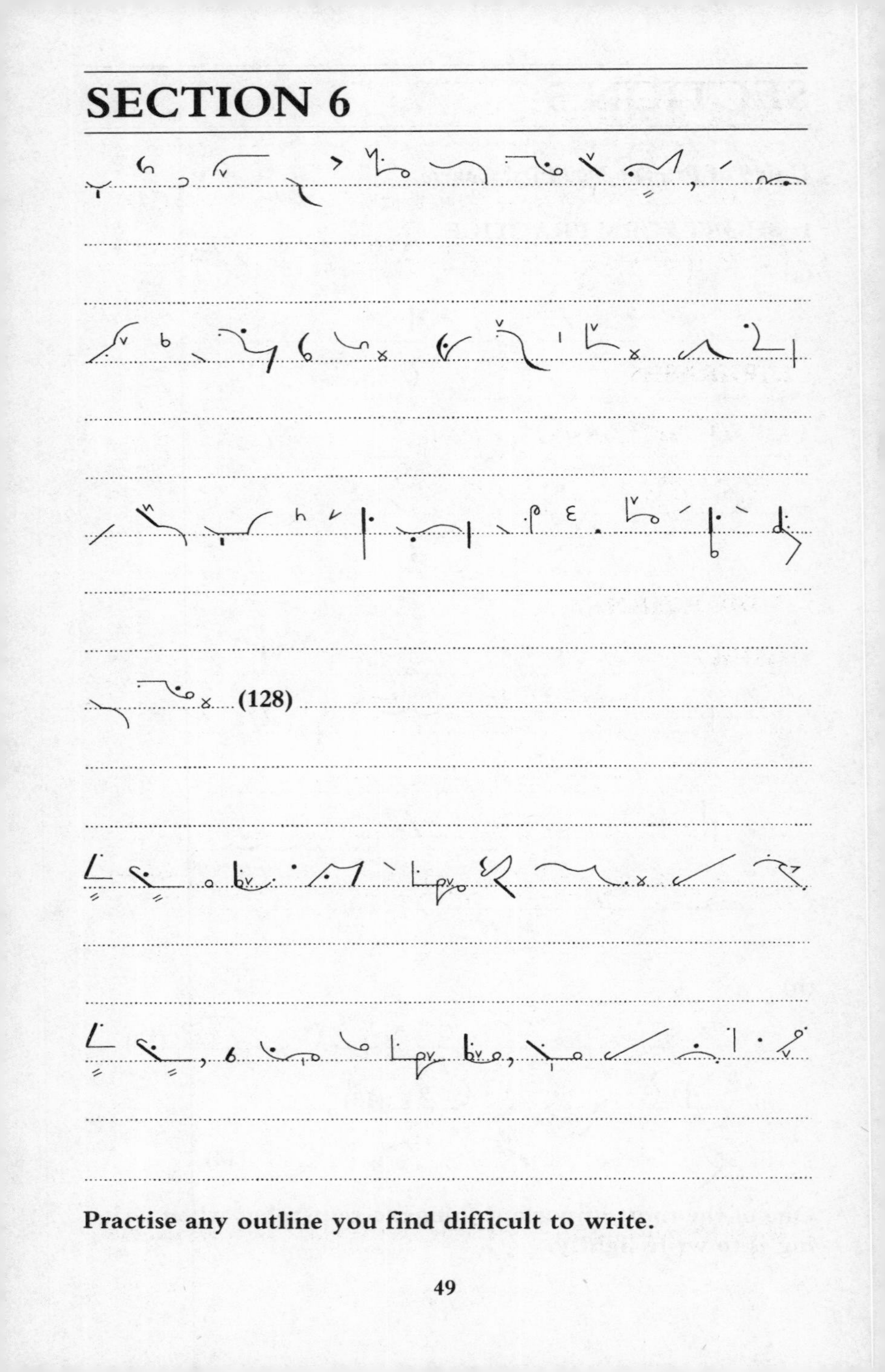

SECTION 6

(128)

Practise any outline you find difficult to write.

SECTION 5

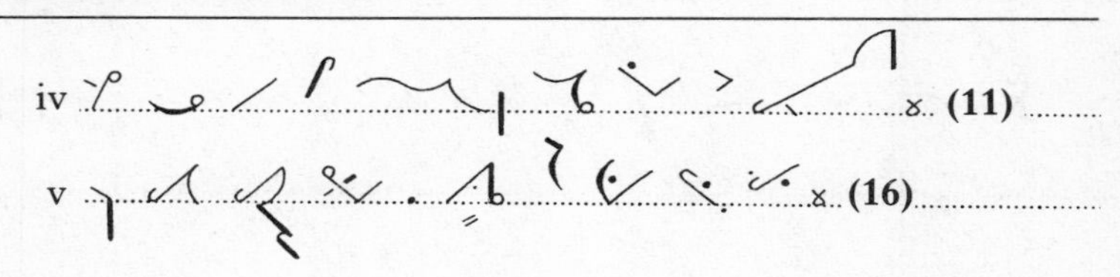

2 PHRASES

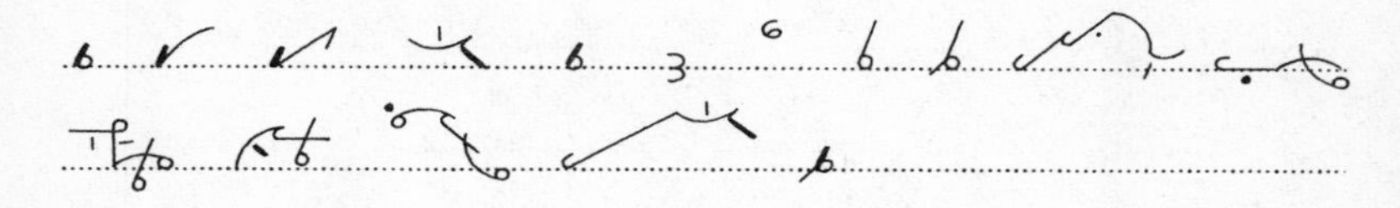

3 DICTATION

(a) Easy

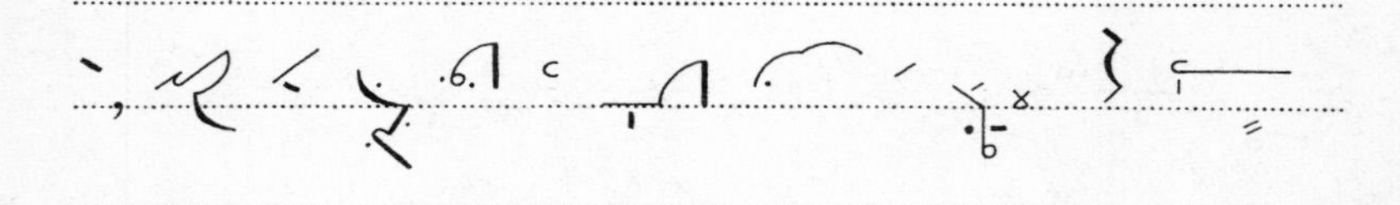

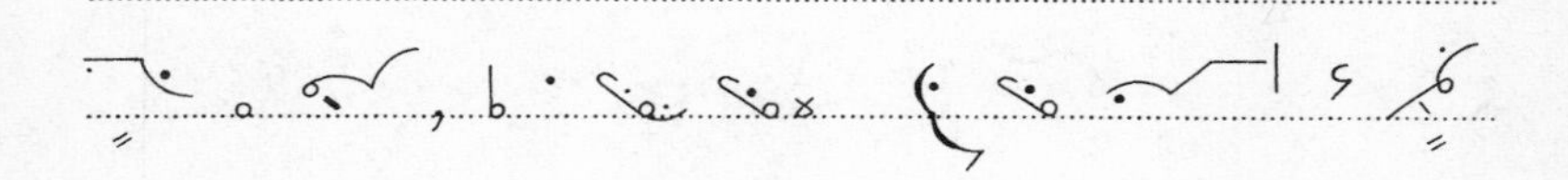

Hold the pen lightly. Writing shorthand is a delicate craft.

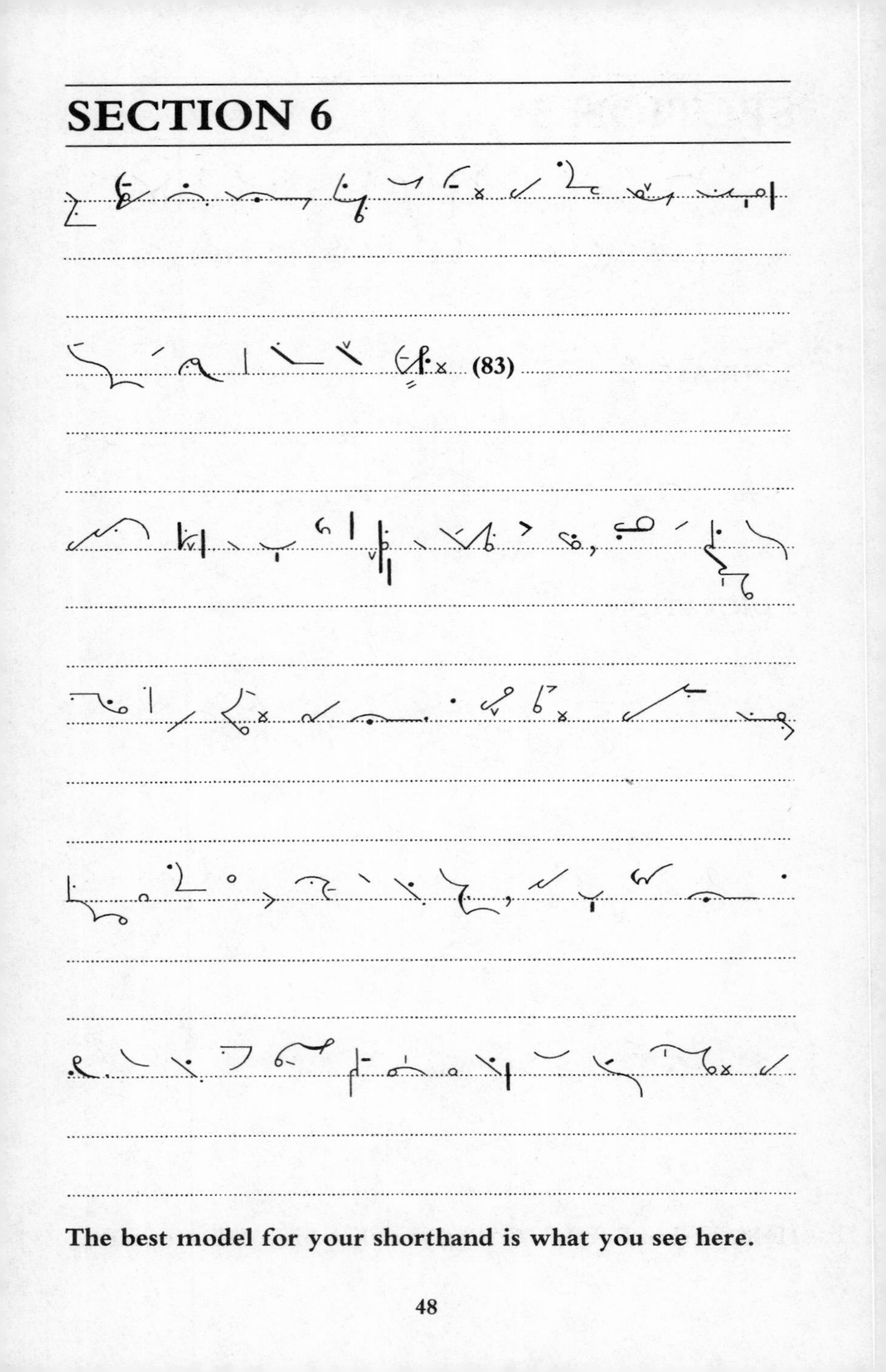

SECTION 6

(83)

The best model for your shorthand is what you see here.

SECTION 5

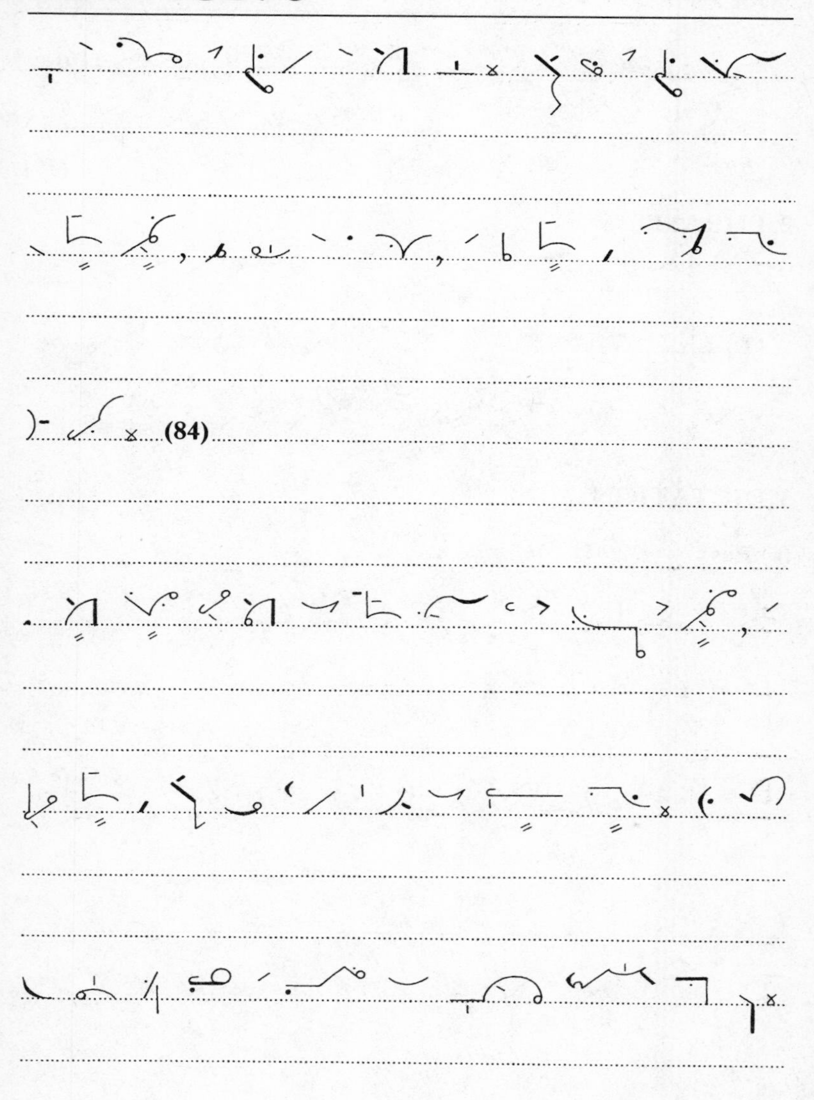

Relax—then you can write lightly.

SECTION 6

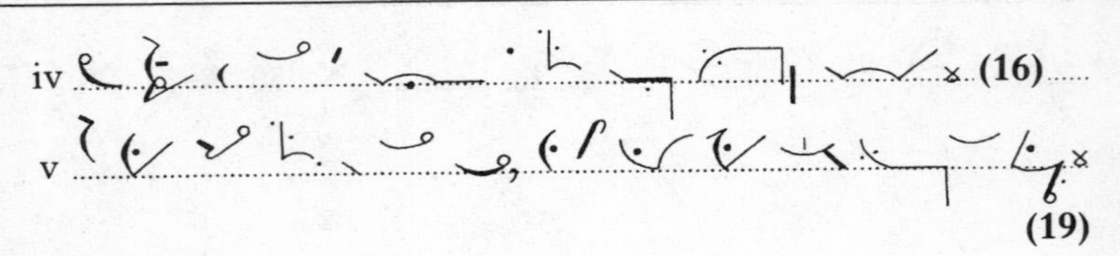

2 PHRASES

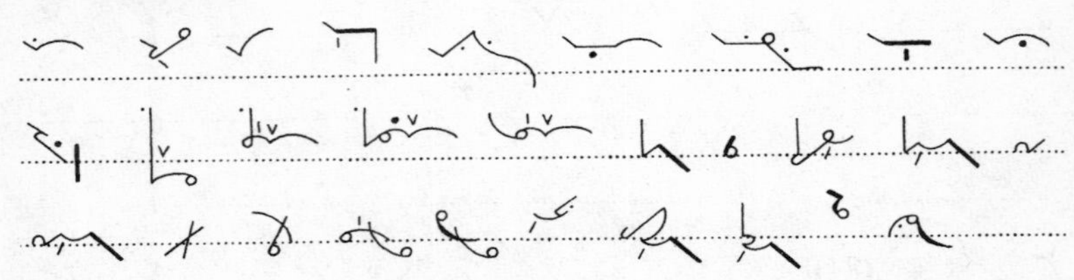

3 DICTATION

(a) Easy

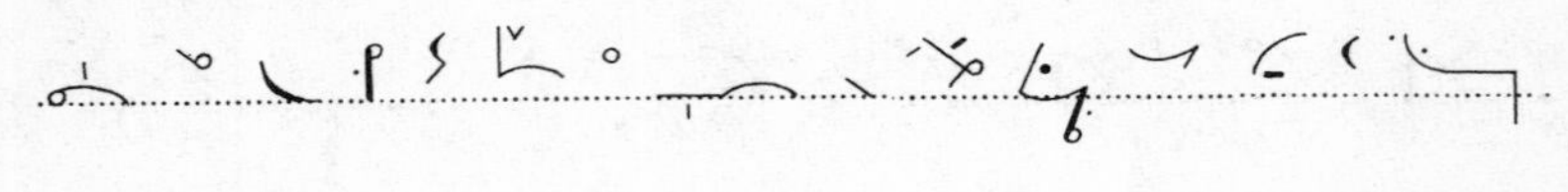

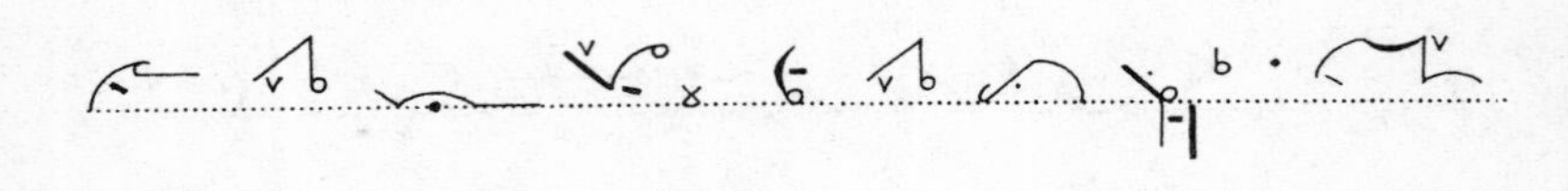

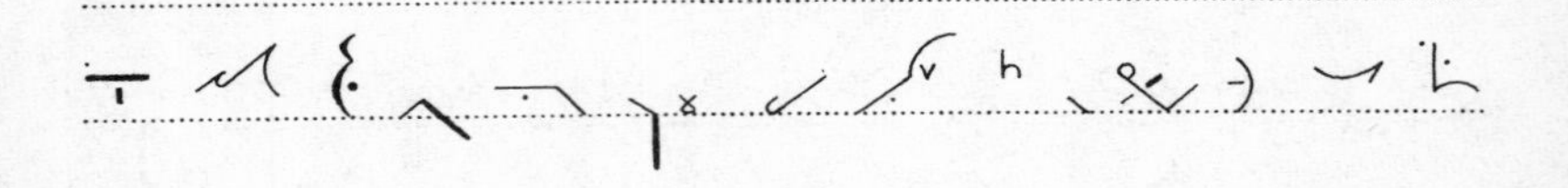

Hook *L* and Hook *R* are small and round.

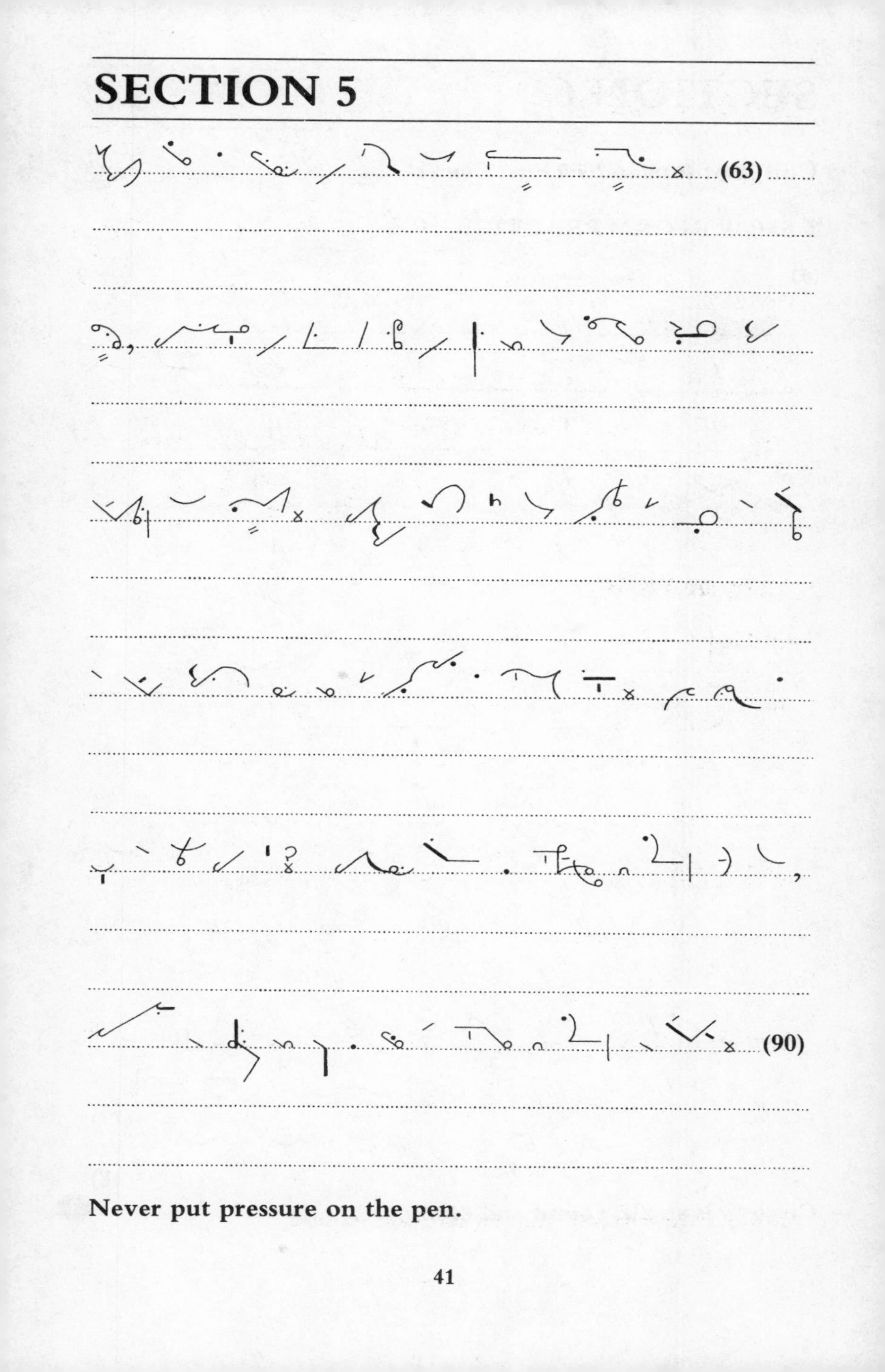

SECTION 5

(63)

(90)

Never put pressure on the pen.

SECTION 6

Unit 10 of *Pitman 2000 First Course*

1 SHORT FORM PRACTICE

(a)

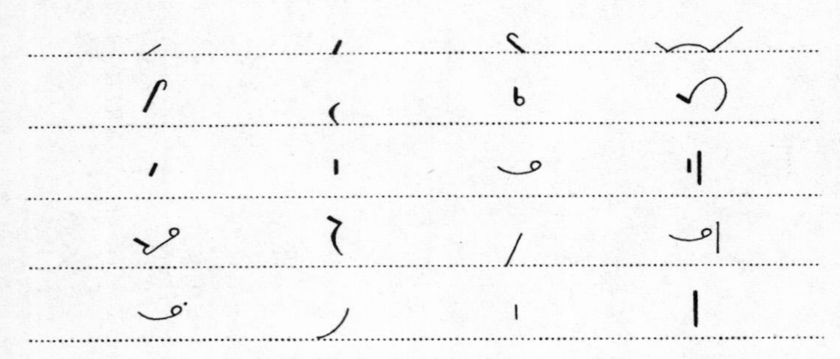

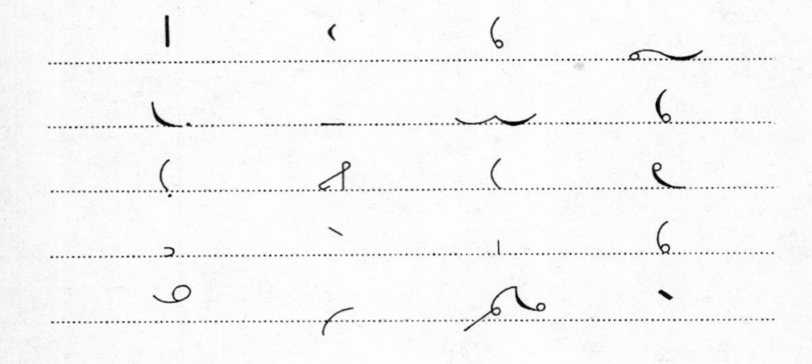

(b)

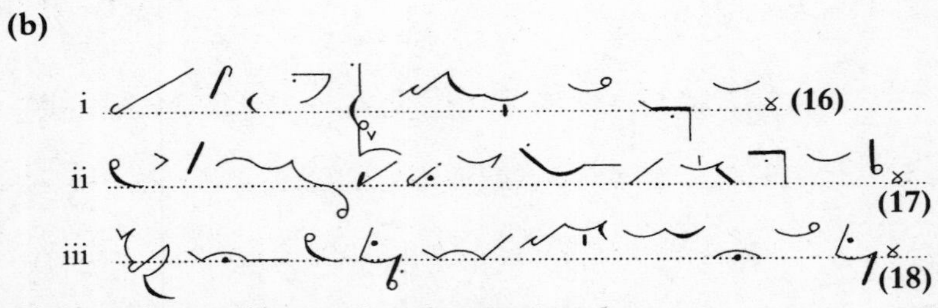

Circle S is small, round and complete.

SECTION 5

(b) Standard

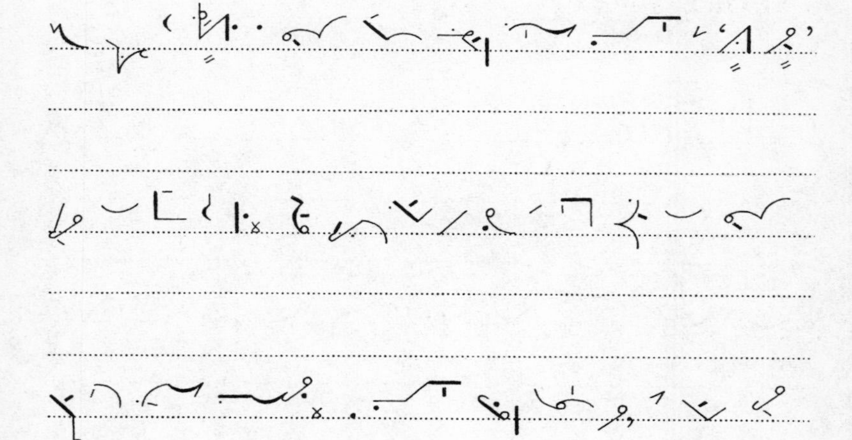

Let the pen glide swiftly over the paper.

SECTION 5

(117)

(57)

Some curves are quarter-circles like *F, V,* and *L*; others are shallow curves like *S, TH,* and *M*.

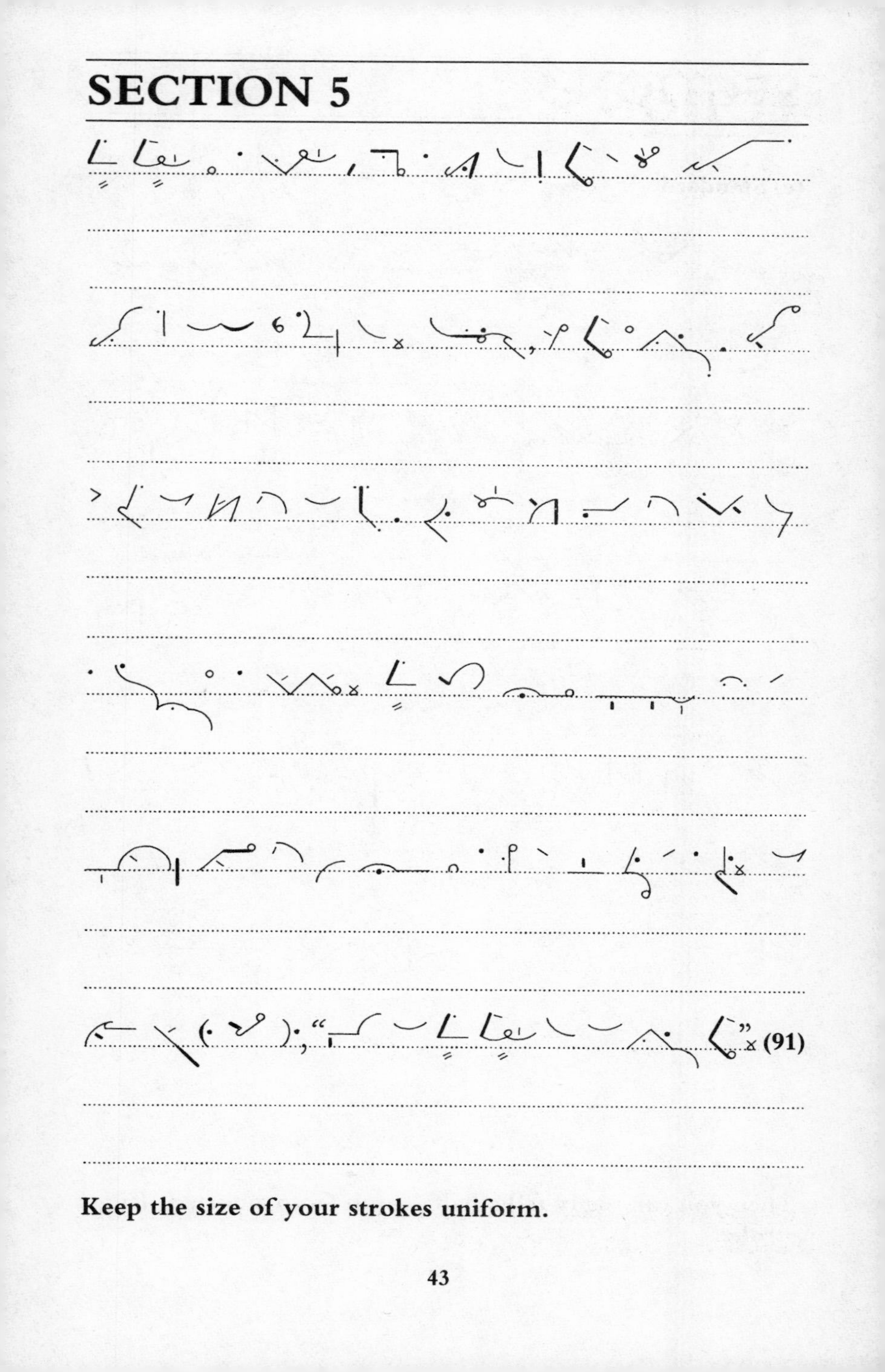

SECTION 5

(91)

Keep the size of your strokes uniform.

SECTION 5

(c) Standard

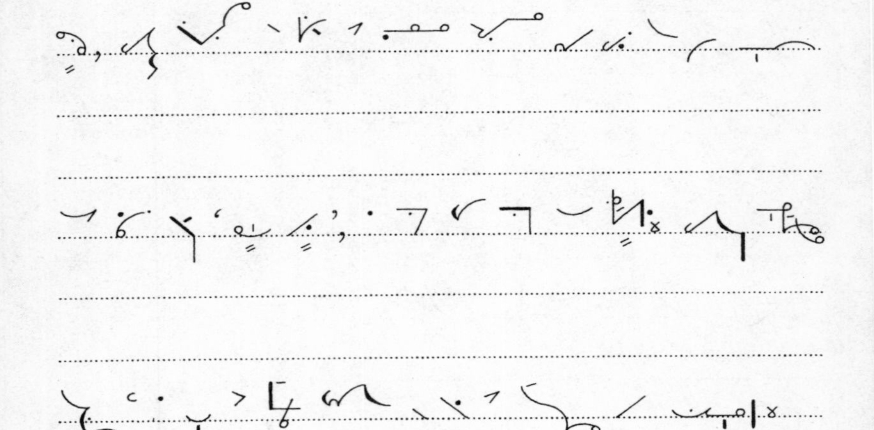

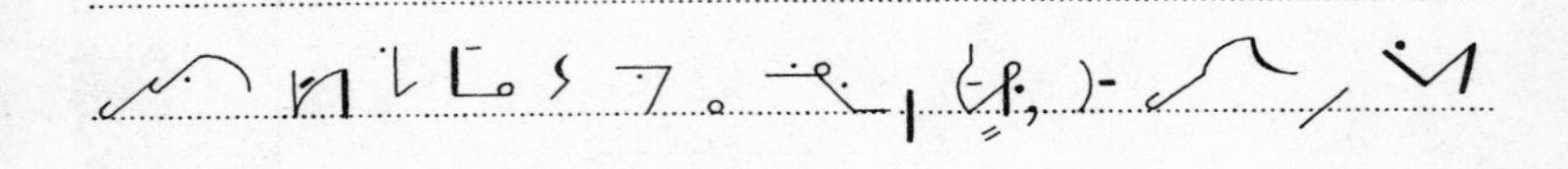

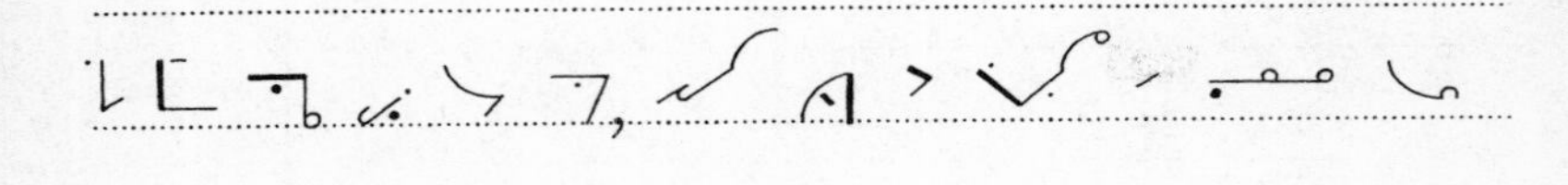

Then you can easily tell a half-length from a normal-length stroke.